Cancer: Cause & Cure

A 20th Century Perspective

Percy Weston

Edited by Andrew Carroll

bôôkbin

NEW ZEALAND NATURAL NUTRITION
FREE PHONE 0800 055 6085
MOBILE: 07765 671350
www.naturesource.co.uk
42a Highland Road,
Norwich, NR2 3NN

BookBin Publishing Pty Ltd
165 Franklin St
Adelaide 5000
South Australia
sales@bookbin.com.au

ISBN 0-9758137-0-6
Cancer: Cause & Cure
A 20th Century Perspective

bôôkbin

The National Library of Australia
Cataloguing-in-Publication entry

Weston, Percy George
Cancer: Cause & Cure. A 20th Century Perspective.

ISBN 0-9758137-0-6

Health & nutrition
641.1
Printed by Hyde Park Press, Adelaide, South Australia

Contents

Section 1

The stuff of life	2	Progress?	44
To catch a rabbit	3	New pesticides	45
Disease repellent	4	A deadly mist	46
My first smoke	5	Partners?	47
Hunger pangs	7	Shattering news	49
Practical advice	8	More drama	51
Headlong into strife	9	A torrid interview	53
College bound	11	A new alarm	55
Dux of class	12	Precise advice	56
The fume cupboard	13	Recovery	59
The Buffalo run	14	Deficiencies	60
Blessing in disguise	16	Animal instinct	61
No longer a drover	17	Conclusive tests on sheep	62
Blue mould alert	18	Adjusting to suit	63
'Expert' help	19	Expansion	64
Milo exposed	20	Devastation	65
The 1932 mouse plague	21	Trapped again	66
Rats in the hay	22	A medical curiosity	67
Yellow dwarf	23	Sterile ewes, 'pregnant' rams	69
Drained of energy	24	Onus of proof	70
Out on my own	25	Highway havoc	71
Primed for emergency	26	Experiments with vitamins	72
Polio strikes	29	Problems licked	74
Disastrous advice	30	The silent killer	76
Chemicals causing arthritis	32	Medical Micawbers	82
The war years	34	A close call	83
Food charts	37	Stranded	84
Cancer takes a hand	40	Home treatment	86
Designer cure	41	Chiropractic	87
The wonder mixture	42	An incredible shock	89

Contents
Section 2

Encounters with animals	92	Curbing cancer culprits	114
Important IACVF meetings	97	A spoonful of sulphur	116
The Ian Gawler case	98	Purging slimy invaders	117
Colds as safety valve	99	Extraordinary	119
All those possible cures	101	Liver colonised	120
The Linxian story	103	Black-walnut tincture	121
Mystery of the viruses	104	The future	122
Is no food safe?	105	Publisher's footnote	123
Dr Joel Wallach	106	Appendix A	126
Why supplements?	108	Appendix B	132
Antioxidants	109	Appendix C	136
Foods causing cancer	111	Appendix D	151
Tobacco home truths	112	*Cancer-Fighting Foods*	157

DEDICATION

To Frances and Norman Hooke, of the International Association of Cancer Victors and Friends, who have keep members informed of medical discoveries, problems and controversies surrounding cancer for more than 20 years and have kept me in touch with like-minded people committed to finding a cure. A performance beyond all praise.

INTRODUCTION

A thousand causes of cancer?

IMPROVED sanitation and nutrition this century have undoubtedly increased the lifespan of people in the developed world. We have more creature comforts than at any time in history. Yet many people do not get to enjoy them. They succumb to cancers of every description, even while in the prime of life. Almost everyone can name a family member who has died prematurely and painfully from cancer despite the best efforts of medical science. Being diagnosed as having cancer all too often equates to the death sentence being passed, although surgery and radiation treatment can buy time.

The Collins dictionary defines cancer as *any type of tumour or malignant growth caused by abnormal and uncontrolled cell division. This may spread through the lymphatic system or blood stream to other parts of the body.*

Medical authorities identify seven warning signs: unusual bleeding or discharge, appearance of a lump or swelling, hoarseness or cough, indigestion or difficulty in swallowing, change in bowel habits, a sore that does not heal, or a change in a wart or a mole.

Cancer has been a great puzzle to researchers throughout the world. Each year doctors and biotechnologists spend countless man-hours and untold millions of dollars investigating masses of experimental data. Over the years thousands of things have been named as possible causes of mutations, from toxic stuff and radiation to faulty genes. They may all be right for all I know. But the underlying driving force for that uncontrolled cell division — and therefore its cure — continues to elude the brightest of our scientists. And that hidden knowledge about the stuff of life is what I want to reveal to you, dear reader.

The underlying cause of the elusive and dreaded disease we call cancer, which is also related to arthritis and heart disease, will become obvious to the reader who shares my experiences and observations over a lifetime of struggle on the land. And, more importantly, the reader will come to understand how everybody can beat cancer without expensive drugs, hospitalisation and doctors, just as I have.

Percy George Weston
Eurobin, Victoria

Section 1

THE STUFF OF LIFE

THIS book is not about the rugged individuals I have met on the land (though they deserve a book) or even about the lifestyle of my family and forebears who founded the little farming community of the Ovens Valley where I live.

It is about my attempt to unravel the secrets of nature that might allow us to live in harmony with it, free from pain and disease. In particular it is the story of my encounters over the past century with that powerful and elusive stuff of life, the element phosphorus.

My first contact with the "element of fire", which proved to be so important to an understanding of the nature of cancer and of many other diseases, came in December 1908, when I was five years old. My parents had selected land in a beautiful, quiet valley in north-eastern Victoria called Porepunkah Gully, which ran north for five miles from the Ovens Road, opposite Mount Buffalo.

The house's main source of lighting at night was a kerosene lamp, but my elder sister, Verna, and I used candles in our bedrooms. They were lit by wax matches, and by custom I was allowed to light the candle on my bedroom table, which was just beneath the window. The day had been hot and windows and doors were left open for the cool evening breeze to blow gently through the house. On this occasion the breeze was stronger than usual and blew out the candle.

When a small boy strikes a match, his nose is never far from the point of combustion, which invariably means inhaling the fumes. I struck the match, but the breeze blew it out as I moved it toward the candle wick. First breath. I tried again, with the same result. Second breath. By cupping my hands to shelter the match until it was well alight and shielding the flame until the candle was lit, I succeeded. But not before inhaling more of the fumes given off by the wax matches. By the time I had taken off my clothes and put on pyjamas, the world seemed a strange place. I felt I was floating in space.

Frightened, I got out of bed to rush out to my parents — and immediately fell over. Unable to stand, I crawled into the living room on hands and knees. My mother snapped, "Get up off the floor!" As I tried to, I fell over again, partly paralysed. There was pandemonium in the house that night. My parents picked me up and placed me limp and dazed in the old rocking chair. They put my feet in a dish of warm water, gave me a dose of brandy, and carried me to bed, none the wiser about what had gone wrong with me. Next morning I was very weak and had a terrible headache. The reader will note the havoc unleashed on an unsuspecting small boy by three match heads impregnated with phosphorus.

TO CATCH A RABBIT

R ABBITS were introduced to Victoria in 1859 via Thomas Austin's Western District property of Barwon Park in 1859 and, with few natural enemies, they quickly spread. In north-eastern Victoria by 1910 they were in plague proportions and competing with the native animals and our farm animals for feed. Various methods were used at various times in the rabbits' breeding cycle to curb their numbers: trapping, poisoning, fumigating, netting fences, and even the use of ferrets. The favored method, and for us the most successful, was to lay poison baits for them. I would help my father in this enterprise at the age of seven.

The rabbit bait was made by dissolving a stick of phosphorus in a gallon (4.5 litres) of boiling water and adding bran, pollard (a wheat bran) and brown sugar to make a stiff dough which was put in a container. Usually the bait was put out by a horse-drawn cart. As it was drawn along, the cart dug a shallow furrow into which small lumps were dropped at regular intervals. Where the terrain was steep, one had first to make a scrape with a hoe or shovel. This was done by my father, and my job would be to mould small lumps of bait in my fingers and drop them in.

Inevitably I got a whiff of the phosphorus in the bait, but I soon got the knack of keeping upwind of it. The fumes, as with the wax matches, caused nausea and headache that could last for hours. Needless to say, rabbit baiting was not one of my favorite pastimes. The reaction of the rabbits is worth mentioning. Our home overlooked a small creek flat on a neighbor's property where rabbits abounded. One day, after the neighbor had spread poison there, my brother Eric and I watched from about 100 metres away to see how the rabbits fared. Within an hour 20 rabbits were sampling the baits.

When they had eaten two or three baits, they would stagger about and disappear into cover along the creek. Most of the females made for their burrows, but we noticed three bucks retire to squats in clumps of long grass. After a few minutes we approached to see if they were dead. The first looked as if ready to bolt, but as we moved closer and closer he made no move, and at last we could pick him up. The others too were in their squats, alive and looking as if ready to bolt, but made little or no attempt to run. Their bodies were limp. They were paralysed.

DISEASE REPELLENT

MY mother, Catherine Ester Fitzgerald, was the youngest of four girls in a family of 10 children. She was born in 1870 on or close to the Buckland goldfield, a place known in the history books by an alternative name, the Valley of Death. Her mother, my grandmother Margaret Keane, was governess to the children of the Member for Beechworth in the Victorian Parliament and had come out from County Galway, Ireland. She and my grandfather, James Fitzgerald, met at a social function in Beechworth and married soon afterwards. He came from St John, Newfoundland, and was one of the Forty-niners who went to the Sacramento Valley, California, at the start of the gold rush of 1849 and worked on the diggings for three or four years. When word came that gold had been discovered in Australia, he and a party of 70 adventurers chartered a ship from San Francisco and set sail for Sydney. And when they got to Sydney they carried their swags across to Beechworth.

James Fitzgerald struck it rich on the Buckland, at Golden Point. He and his party of five took out five separate claims and worked them together, with Fitzgerald selecting the third of these claims in November, 1853. Each got about 15 ounces of gold a week for three months. They worked right down to solid rock, where the good coarse gold was. A few places on Buckland allowed them to get down to the old river bottom without being flooded out.

The discovery of gold in the Buckland in 1853 attracted some 5,000 mainly Caucasian diggers from the pre-federation Australian colonies and further afield. They were soon joined by 2,000 Chinese, mainly from Canton and gold fields in the USA and elsewhere. At that time the part played by sanitation, clean water and fresh food in controlling disease was little appreciated and, in the primitive, crowded conditions on the diggings with excrement seeping into the river, diseases such as typhoid/typhus, diphtheria, cholera and sandy blight flourished. The normal European tucker consisted of mutton, pickles, damper, black tea, and native birds and animals — no vegetables or fruit. The diet, cleanliness and consequently resistance of the Chinese was slightly better, although their staple food of polished rice (with the vitamins lost in the polishing) was a mixed blessing; they seem mainly to have suffered from the thiamin (vitamin B1) deficiency known as beri beri.

Visitors to the Buckland cemetery can be puzzled by its unusual appearance. The front half contains headstones and unmarked graves. The back half, which is nicely levelled, is apparently empty. In fact some 2000 whites lie buried there in a mass grave, cut off in the prime of life by the epidemics. Their exact origins will never be known. (There were many more Chinese deaths later, of course, in the infamous massacre of 1857; they were not buried here but unceremoniously where they fell.)

Remarkably, my mother's family was the only one in the district to go through all those perilous pioneering years without loss of a member. They gave credit for their survival to clean drinking water and the use of sulphur compounds as a disease repellent. And these methods were handed on to us. As soon as her own children reached school age, my mother had us line up every Saturday morning for a drink of lemon and Epsom salts or a teaspoon of Golden Syrup and powdered sulphur. (This was made up from a packet of Epsom salts dissolved in a jug of lemon water, and two teaspoons of powdered sulphur mixed in half a cup of Golden Syrup.) Consequently, at a time when there were a lot of diseases about and you could count on one or other of your classmates to be away with colds, influenza or diphtheria, none of us lost a day of school at Eurobin in eight years.

MY FIRST SMOKE

MY father, George Weston, was born in 1869, the eighth in a family of 10 children. His father, Albert Dürer Weston, came from Shropshire, England, and was so named in fond memory of the German master painter and engraver Albrecht Dürer who, as family legend would have it, often stayed with the Westons on visits to England. (The great man and my grandfather never actually met, being separated by about three centuries!) Albert Weston married my grandmother, Janie Jones, in Melbourne.

My parents met at a dance, either at Bright or Porepunkah. About that time George Weston was cutting the track to Buffalo with his brother, my uncle Bill. And in Porepunkah Gully, where the tree trunks grew four to five feet thick, they felled timber for gold mining. The wood they cut fired the boiler of Brady's Confidence Dredge, with steam being used to work the bucket and chain. Dredging for gold ended on the river in 1919, after some 25 years.

In my childhood days my mother would take her young family at least once a month to visit her ageing parents and other members of the Fitzgerald family who lived at the old homestead. In the hooded buggy drawn by a strong horse, it took nearly two hours to get there. Generally my father came too. With Eric and Mervyn, who were both younger than my sister and I, riding up front in the false seat, it was a comfortable and exhilarating journey. We would generally go on a Saturday, preferably when there was to be a moon to light the way home. I have occasion to remember one visit there, when I was about 10, very well.

My grandfather smoked a pipe and uncles Jim and Percy, after whom I was named, were very keen smokers of the *Milo* brand of cigarette, then imported from the USA in large quantities. They were made up from the famous golden-colored Virginian tobacco leaf. Long before that year (1912), possibly for half a century, the yellow-leaf cigarette tobacco was being produced in the USA but the methods used drew little attention. They were, from what I could glean, the same methods we in Australia were to adopt in the 1930s to grow our yellow-leaf tobacco.

My uncles often tempted me to "have a smoke" but my parents always objected. These *Milo* cigarettes had a delicious aroma and, thus enticed on this occasion, I pinched a couple from an open packet and smuggled them home. Then one evening after tea I walked to a quiet gully some 300 metres from the house and lit up. Like many a small boy having a first smoke, I received a rude surprise. The first part was easy. You draw in small amounts of smoke and blow out through your nose. Then you try to do the "draw back". That was the surprise. I tried it and immediately became so giddy and weak that I fell to the ground and began to wonder if I could get home. It must have been an hour or more before I was able to walk back in my delicate condition, sneak in by the back way to my room, and climb into bed. I was still feeling "a bit" sick for most of the next day, and again my parents were left wondering why.

I took up smoking standard (brown leaf) tobacco in 1922, and never heard of anyone suffering ill effects after lighting up. I was unable to account for the Milo experience till I learned how to grow yellow-leaf tobacco with superphosphate in the 1930s.

HUNGER PANGS

L IFE became more strenuous from the age of 12. In the summer months three or four cows had to be milked before and after school. Apart from a walk or run of two miles to school, games such as football or cricket at playtime exacted a good deal of energy. Thus I would often arrive home tired and famished. As my mother would never allow us a snack when a good meal was soon to be served up, there was no alternative but to raid the garden or orchard.

Percy Weston's mother feeds the chooks in the yard of the family home

Garden peas were first available in early November, but consuming 10 or 12 pods of half-ripe peas usually gave me a headache. Cherries, peaches and plums were next in season, and presented no ill-effects. In February early apples and sweet corn (maize) appeared on my menu. Apples never gave trouble, but a feast of raw, milky sweet corn always brought on a headache. By May our walnuts had been harvested and dried, and I'd eat eight or 10 at a time; always they produced a vicious headache. (They were so tasty and satisfying, I used to eat too many.)

In the winter months I relished the bran which we bought from the mill for fowl food. Here again, a little too much would bring on a headache, whereas the rather sour oranges from our seedling trees produced no such side-effects. All through the teenage years, some foods gave me days of great discomfort. The main ones responsible were bran foods for breakfast and egg dishes, and a big meal of large white mushrooms gave me the worst time ever. It was not until 1934, when I happened on an analysis of our common foods in a chart that I suspected the cause of such food sensitivity.

The school leaving age in those early days was 14. I obtained my Merit Certificate at Eurobin State School in December, 1916, when still only 13, which meant I had to stay on for a further year of schooling. Not that I minded; I wasn't sure what I wanted to do with my life. To make 1917 worthwhile, the new teacher, Miss Estelle Jorgsimson, who had replaced Mr James Mills Scott on his retirement, suggested she could coach me for a Junior State Scholarship, of which 20 were on offer that year. And so I became candidate No.376. The school holidays were spent helping my father. Farm work included hand-planting of 10 acres of potatoes and cultivating the 15 acres of maize with a horse-drawn scarifier.

PRACTICAL ADVICE

GEORGE Weston, my father [born 1869], was a very practical farmer and a hard worker. And he picked a good spot for farming in the Porepunkah Gully, which can pull more clouds and mist than any other valley in the district. He had farming methods more scientific than ones in use today. He was a perfectionist and always thinking ahead. Livestock he could produce and keep in very good condition; they were always well fed, with plenty of hay in store. And I never saw him grow a bad crop in his life. The soil was thoroughly prepared, and it was done with horses and a double-furrow plough. (Horses did not compact the ground and destroy the aerobics and worms.) He preserved seed in the best form to produce a quick start and never ploughed the ground until the autumn break had come. When all the non-crop seed was struck, they were just turned under to make fertiliser. Today, instead of burying weeds at the outset, farmers use all sorts of weed poisons to keep down their growth in crops.

My father had an acute sense of timing; he would put in a crop when he knew conditions were ideal. For example, potatoes and tomatoes never went into a hot soil. If we made a mistake he was quick to pick us up. Before going into partnership with him, as I will describe later, I often worked with him after school and in the May holidays. I had such a good natural tuition that I think I avoided many mistakes. (For example, I see too many farmers who sit on the tractor and go round and round the paddock making a great big saucer of it. This gives no drainage and leaves a furrow on the outside to act as a levy bank; it will gather the water and rot the wheat. Too many crops today have wet feet. These lazy, ignorant farmers are getting only half or two-thirds' production, and the soil degradation they're causing is tragic. The correct method is to put furrows across the paddock about 30 yards apart.)

George Weston was well able to discern a problem and counter it from practical experience but he had virtually no formal education.

HEADLONG INTO STRIFE

THE year 1918 opened with calamities but eased into much changed surroundings for me and a different way of life. Having, as I thought, finished school, and in accordance with my father's wish that I get some cattle-droving experience, I saddled up a young mare. She was newly broken in and flighty. My father's idea was to harden her up for stock work, away from familiar haunts, by my riding her down to the lower paddock along the Ovens Road. As I took her there she pranced and nervously skied at objects unfamiliar. Just opposite Eurobin railway station the sight of an old rusty bucket in a deep table drain caused her to jump suddenly sideways and displace the saddle. Soon she was bucking in circles in a frenzy. As I pulled on the right rein to straighten her, she lost her footing, and horse and rider somersaulted into the stone-hard drain. I landed on my head.

George Weston, who must have been following my progress from his vantage point on the spring cart, picked me up, unconscious, and drove me in his vehicle alongside the bags of seed potatoes to our home. I remained unconscious for most of the next 12 hours. My next vivid memory is being caught by my mother with my head under the garden tap trying to cool off. The doctor was called in and diagnosed the painful throbbing as being due to a fractured skull. I was packed off for a couple of weeks with my Uncle Jim and Aunty Mary at the Fitzgerald home on Buckland, and put on light duties while the fracture mended. (By this time my Uncle Percy had moved to Melbourne and was working for a stone mason, which was work that came second nature to him after years of experience in mining.)

Two or three days later my cousin, Bill Weston, with a local man for company, called on my cattleman uncle Jim for news of stock movements. The Fitzgerald and Weston cattle runs were adjoining. They wanted to check on the Weston cattle, which they had been unable to take down to the sales in November after spring floods had washed away all bridges crossing the Buffalo River. (Bill's father was my Uncle Bill [born 1857] who had two other sons, Ernie and Charlie Weston.) As we had seen none of Bill's cattle, they rode on to spend the night at the Weston hut on Buffalo River, a round trip of 30 miles. Soon they were to return in dismay. Late next morning as the horses were rested and allowed to feed, Bill and his companion were alarmed to sight a huge black column of smoke some five miles down river. It was being fanned by a hot northerly wind and the valley was being transformed as they watched into a raging tunnel of smoke and flame. With the bush tinder-dry, they sensed they could be trapped by the fire and burnt to death. They ran to catch their horses and rode bareback at full gallop to a swampy area two miles upstream. Though nearly suffocated by smoke, they were untouched by the fire, which passed all around the swamp. After it was safe to move out, they were relieved to find that the hut was spared.

That evening it was still too hot and dangerous to search for cattle, so they conducted a wide search in the morning, but found no cattle, alive or dead. With no feed available for the horses, they headed home while I assisted in making firebreaks around the Fitzgerald property to counter the fire as it burned slowly downhill into the Buckland Valley. Jim Fitzgerald had to muster his cattle off the divide and seek agistment, for the fire burnt all feed as it passed along. Cousin Bill and his friend went back to the Buffalo River run three days later, searched far and wide but 200 head of his cattle had gone. They concluded the cattle had been stolen, and reported the theft to police. But who started the fire and why? The only clue we had to go on was that a shady character had left evidence of having camped in the Weston hut a few months before. I didn't know it then, but the incident would have fateful consequences.

COLLEGE BOUND

DURING the third week in January 1918, doctors visited Buckland to inoculate all people there against the lethal "Spanish" pneumonic influenza epidemic that was spreading around the world and was set to become a pandemic. I was among those to receive a shot of vaccine. Very soon I received an urgent message to return home to Eurobin. Results of the scholarship had been published and my name was entered at No.16 on the winners' list! My mother wasted no time in going off to the big city, Melbourne, to buy clothes and select a school where I could be sent as a boarder. (Melbourne in those days was many hours' travel away by train.)

On the 11th February 1918, I found myself entering the gates of Xavier College . . . and the very week after classes began I was confined, along with 10 other boys, in the big infirmary. We had all contracted the dreaded 'flu! And it *was* dreadful: two boys died from it. Prayers were said daily for the rest of us and we recovered. Five weeks elapsed before we could return to classes. I consider myself fortunate to have been inoculated. Millions who weren't had no resistance and died of pneumonia within days of contracting the flu, which could be spread by a sneeze or a cough. All told about 30 million people died of flu that year and in 1919, making it possibly the most devastating outbreak in history.

It was while I was in the sick bay that a letter came from my mother informing me of the murder of Barclay, the manager of the Wannangatta station and that his employee, Bamford, was missing. The Wannangatta run adjoined the Weston cattle run. There was some speculation, she added, that the murder was concerned with the theft of the Weston cattle. The police suspected Bamford, who could not be found, though his horse was located out where he had been repairing a fence.

DUX OF CLASS

THE bout of influenza had branded me a weakling with the school authorities. But while banned from sports, I was assured of plenty of time for study and I decided to make the most of it. While I could manage only fourth in the test at the end of first term, I came second at the end of second term, and by December, 1918, I was dux of the class of 34. Still the spring of 1918 was a very sad one for me. First Ernie Weston, who had been in the landing at Gallipoli and had gone all through he war, was reported killed by a sniper's bullet in Palestine. And in October, 1918, his brother Charlie died of influenza, the second wave of the dreaded epidemic, during desert patrol in Palestine.

There was also news that Bamford had been found murdered at Mount Howett station, his body uncovered by dingoes. Bamford and Barclay must have intercepted the cattle duffers droving a big mob, including the Weston cattle. For the thieves, a five-year jail term could only have been avoided by starting the fire in the Buckland Valley to conceal the theft and by silencing Barclay and Bamford, who could identify them.

As a student I was pretty conscientious. I have fond memories of my years at Xavier, and of the people who taught me, especially Fr Peter Ignatius Baker, who inspired me greatly. We had a wide variety of subjects at the beginning, and in the spare period I studied Agricultural Science. For the Leaving Certificate year I had to decide, in consultation with my parents, what to do with my life. I opted for a career in medicine. To prepare for it, it was decided that I should study chemistry, physics, biology, Latin, and three subjects in mathematics for the final two years of school.

THE FUME CUPBOARD

M Y introduction to the science of chemistry began dramatically in 1921 in the first week of term. It happened in the chemistry lab where a senior boy was carrying out experiments to test the properties of phosphorus pentoxide. The laboratory had a special ventilated glass cabinet, or fume cupboard, to isolate such experiments involving poisonous gases, and he was following correct procedure in using it. I saw him ignite a pea-sized piece of phosphorus in oxygen inside the cabinet. He then went to seal it off by closing the vertical sliding door, and it jammed. As he fumbled to close the door, gas billowed from the cabinet. He must have inhaled plenty. In 10 seconds he had collapsed on the floor. Other students grabbed his arms and dragged and carried him outside. The chemistry master put the lab off-limits until the gas dispersed. We were told the boy was close to death. Fortunately, he recovered. His limp condition reminded me of those rabbits back home similarly immobilised by the phosphorus-soaked baits.

(An incident similar to the one at my college was reported in the *Border Morning Mail* as happening a few years ago at Wodonga High School. Again it occurred in the lab, only this time the exposure came about as the result of a practical joke. A student used food tongs to take white phosphorus out of its covering of water and allowed it to flame as he walked round the room. Within minutes most students were struggling on the floor, and 17 were admitted to hospital. Some were still recovering there days later.)

This, as I say, was my introduction to chemistry in 1921. My class was not due to study phosphorus (symbol 'P') till later in the year, but I was curious to know more. I turned to the chapter in the textbook and read that phosphorus is a volatile element which forms soluble compounds and its gases are extremely poisonous. Phosphorus pentoxide, for example, is a powerful dehydrating agent, which attacks the moist tissue of the nose, mouth, throat and lungs and causes paralysis. There was also mention of a weird and fatal disease known as *phossey jaw*, which was linked to exposure to white phosphorus. Many of its victims worked in the factories that had made our wax matches of recent memory before safety matches were invented. It said they had died terrible deaths.

• CHEMISTRY CALLS

I WAS fond of science at school, and I had my heart set on going straight to Melbourne University to study medicine. As my family was not wealthy, my plan was to get high enough marks in 1922 to become dux of the school, which carried a well-endowed scholarship to Newman College. I put in nine months of intensive study in order to win the distinction by, I hoped, at least 40 marks. Come the exams to decide the dux of the school, I was all prepared. Or so I thought. In the pure-maths paper there was a group of questions I had never studied. They were not dealt with at all in my text book. Instead of the text prescribed by the university, I had been issued at the start of the year with the wrong book! A notice posted after the exam showed that I had missed out on the scholarship by one mark.

It seems that I was destined never to be a doctor, for worse was to follow. Just before the public exams began on December 1st, an epidemic of mumps [*paramyxovirus*] swept through the college. I went up to the Exhibition Building with a towel bound round my head, a face like a full moon, and a numbing headache. Though I passed in all subjects, no other scholarship came my way after the results were published in the newspapers. Perhaps I could have got a part-time job to help finance my way through tertiary study, but that was all academic now. My father had suffered a financial reverse, and I was needed back home. So ended my school days.

THE BUFFALO RUN

H OW had this sudden and career-changing emergency arisen? Well, I believe it can be linked to the Mt Howett murders and earlier disappearance of 200 Weston cattle. In 1921 the Westons decided to restock the Buffalo River run by buying up some 300 young steers at a Myrtleford sale. It took Eric and Bill Weston two days to drive this big mob on to the run in May 1921, to eat off the heavy growth of pasture. Every month Eric and Bill rode out to keep watch over the cattle and to provide salt in the paddock near the hut to keep the steers from wandering too far. In early 1922 they were surprised to find a group of four prospectors camped near the head of Nelson Creek. As the Westons met up with them at least six times, they got to know their names and how the work of gold mining was progressing. I saw for myself various members of this foursome when I was taken to cattle sales.

The autumn of 1922 was dry and tough on stock, so it was decided to reduce numbers. About 50 of the biggest steers were drafted off and taken to a Myrtleford sale. Only a poor price was offered, so the steers were driven back to the run. During the cold winter months of 1922 the four men were missing from the claim at Nelson Creek, but they were back in the spring when good pasture growth had caused cattle prices to soar.

The Westons decided to sell 100 or so steers in the late November sale at the Myrtleford market, but when Eric and Bill rode down to the run to muster them, none could be found. The prospectors were missing from Nelson's Creek, too. A widespread search turned up fewer than 10 of the 300 head from the Buffalo River run. Police stations through NE Victoria were alerted but all inquiries over two years at saleyards proved fruitless. However, Bill Weston kept a close watch on all cattle sales listed in the farming paper, the *Weekly Times*, and one day his eye chanced upon a mare impounded at Mansfield that bore his brand. The mare had disappeared along with the cattle. Inquiries among outback farms near Mansfield revealed that a big mob of steers had passed through headed for Stratford in Gippsland, where auctioneers admitted they had sold a big mob brought in by northern drovers, but had kept no brands or earmarks. Police then requested a written detailed description of each of the four drovers, which identified them with the men of Nelson Creek. But they were unable to find the men and so solve, Eric and Bill reckoned, the Mt Howett murders as well.

In the 1850s and 1860s cattle duffing and horse thieving were rife in northern Victoria, and the exploits of one Bogong Jack were legendary. He would take horses from our region and drive them over the mountains and down a perilous track into Gippsland to be sold on the quiet. And in the 1920s at least one bush poet knew where Bogong Jack's trail led, as a glance through a recently published anthology* shows.

Billy Wye: the last true Australian bush poet, Dianne Carroll, ed., 304pp, Carroll Publishing 1997, available through BookBin

It was our visitor at the hut, Billy Wye. He was a wizard with words, as he proved in this introduction to his poem "Mountain Memories".

'T was when I camped in Weston's Hut upon the Buffalo River;
The rain and hail rang on the roof and snow winds made me shiver.
The mountain creeks were brimming full, the river ran a banker,
So like a schooner in distress, I was compelled to anchor.

I well remember winters when I was a boy. The temperature would go down to -18° Fahrenheit (-28°C). It is milder today, some 10-12 degrees warmer. As a result of global warming there is barely any snow on Mount Buffalo now. They're lucky to get 6 inches (15cm) on Buffalo where they used to get 6 feet (183cm).

BLESSING IN DISGUISE

AFTER the loss of the 300 steers, I had to give up all thought of a profession. I returned to the land and I have remained there ever since . . . without ever losing my love for chemistry, which has helped me solve many practical problems. Looking back down through the arches of the years, it now seems a blessing in disguise that I escaped the pipeline of a medical career. I mean that constricted system of clinical observation and double-blind trials, of testing and analysis far removed from the daily challenges of growing plants and nurturing farm animals.

Had I continued unschooled in the ways of nature, there is no doubt I would have died many years ago from so-called natural causes. And in those shortened years as a doctor I would have dithered about trying to find cures for diseases that still baffle the medical world. I would have missed seeing the bigger picture. With my indispensable grounding in the sciences, I was providentially delivered into the complex, vibrant realm of nature. It was a realm in which important discoveries came about almost casually, so that the reader will be amazed how simple nature's remedies turn out to be. The farm was to become my living laboratory.

In five years at Xavier College in Melbourne I never lost touch with the land. I wrote to my parents regularly and came home at school holidays to take part in any farm work of the day. Thus when money was tight and help was needed with a heavy schedule of mixed farming, a partnership with my father and brother was the logical outcome.

On returning home in mid-December 1922, my first task was to cultivate and weed our first crop of tobacco, and then to plant and look after several acres of potatoes. Tobacco was a crop with great promise, both for financial security and job creation, and lacked the controversy that surrounds it today. There was no suggestion of tobacco causing cancer in smokers then, and with good reason — it didn't. Its role as a causative agent came later and had much to do with changes in the way it was grown and processed, as I will explain. I can speak from first-hand experience because I was involved in the industry in Australia from its infancy.

NO LONGER A DROVER

THE Westons have been graziers of the High Plains country of south-eastern Australia since the 1880s. But I was unable to continue the family tradition due to an accident on New Year's eve in 1926, when I was 22. At the time I was dressed in my Sunday best. Going down to nearby Myrtleford to attend a social evening, a concert by notable singers of the district, I was thrown off my bicycle. The front wheel came off at the top of the fork. It landed me face down on the gravel road. Sixteen hours later I awoke in the Myrtleford hospital and wondered

what had become of the concert at which I was to be compere.

I felt in no mood for song as I presided over the spectacle of a fractured skull (again), a huge cut in my forehead, a broken nose, and teeth missing.

Eric Weston and grey, with cattle dog, out droving

Warned that another blow on the head could kill me, I was put to work on the farm crops while my brother Eric did all the stock work and droving to the Bogong High Plains. This was just as well, as full recovery from the accident took at least six months. This accident probably sealed my fate as a farmer.

The summer of 1926-27 saw the beginnings of a dramatic change in the tobacco industry. Until then tobacco [*Nicotiana tabacum*] had been grown naturally, without any fertiliser or spray for insects. When the light-green leaf was harvested and dried in the first primitive kilns, that natural leaf always came out in a brown or mahogany color. It was graded for sale, and tobacco companies made the leaf into either pipe tobacco or roll-your-own, nicely sliced, in packets for the smoker. In those years one never heard of anybody getting lung or throat cancer by smoking this natural tobacco — even though most of the generation of men before me smoked a pipe or rolled their own; some even chewed this tobacco. In the early days no cigarette type was grown.

At first I was wary of smoking tobacco after my early experience with the imported Milo cigarette. However, I soon found that rolling up a half leaf of suitable size to make a cheroot — a small cigar with both ends cut squarely — made a pleasant and relaxing smoke after the evening meal.

BLUE MOULD ALERT

IN 1926 we had an outbreak in our tobacco of the fungus known as *blue mould*. I devised an experiment to see if the mould were flourishing due to the known deficiency of phosphorus in our soils. At planting time in November, I set a row of 120 plants by hand in average soil, using as a starter half a pint (0.3 litre) of water saturated with superphosphate, which is rich in phosphorus. To my surprise, all plants in that row developed the stunted condition known as *yellow dwarf*, whereas the rows alongside grew to the normal two-metre height. The stunted row still succumbed to *blue mould*. All other conditions being equal, I concluded that lack of phosphorus was not a problem, but that a surplus could be —it could paralyse. However, our soils did not have a surplus of this element, not yet anyway. We grew tobacco in the Ovens Valley from 1920 to 1927 without fertilisers and pesticides until growers switched to producing the leaf the way the Americans grew it by applying 500 to 600 pounds of super to the acre.

'EXPERT' HELP

IN mid-1926 the government of the time decided to sponsor cigarette production by finding out how such bright-yellow leaf could be produced here. Four experts were brought from the United States and some local young men sent there for training. A Canadian named Slagg was assigned to carry out trials at our farm, and over two seasons in 1927 he showed us how large quantities of Virginian-type leaf could be grown. The main finding was that at least 500 pounds (227kg) of superphoshate were needed on our land per acre, about which more later.

I had many discussions with him about agriculture and found him to be steeped in the history of tobacco. He said that when Christopher Columbus sailed across to America in 1492 and met up with the Red Indians as he called them, Columbus was amazed when he first saw them blowing smoke from the mouth or nose. When he and they could converse in a crude way he inquired why the Indians smoked, and was told smoking took away fatigue and kept them healthy.

With the knowledge we have of tobacco today, this is easy to explain. The tobacco plant has a very high content of niacin, an essential vitamin in human nutrition. The Indians, Mr Slagg said, had discovered that tobacco helped the digestion of their main foods, meat and corn, and was a wonderful vermifuge. And so smoking or chewing the tobacco leaf was to them a natural part of life.   And when Sir Walter Raleigh introduced tobacco to England, people there were quick to appreciate it, as they lived on a similar diet. As populations increased, so did the use of tobacco. As the demand grew, the eastern seaboard of what is now the USA became the main area of production. This put much pressure on to growers as the sandy soils of Virginia and neighboring states did not yield well. It was found that blood-and-bone fertiliser — abattoir wastes —

would greatly increase yields. But soon demand for them outstripped supply. So any similar waste rich in phosphorus and nitrogen, such as fish meal, was used on tobacco fields as a supplement. To meet shortages of fertiliser, growers looked further afield. They invested in exploiting deposits of guano (bird manure), so much in fact that phosphorus built up in the soils in excess of the plant's needs.

The use of tobacco increased greatly in the 19th century. Seafarers found that, smoked or chewed on long voyages, tobacco could cure or help to prevent scurvy. Back home where many people also relied on a diet of salt meat lacking fresh vegetables, tobacco became an essential (and addictive) source of niacin. Powdered and used as snuff, tobacco was believed even to cure sinus trouble and relieve colds. When grown naturally there were no known health hazards.

To cope with the large demand towards the end of the 19th century, growers began to dry crops in log kilns instead of in the open air. And when supplies of guano and other organic fertilisers ran low, they turned to the new chemical fertilisers, particularly superphosphate. This was made by breaking down the phosphate rock with sulphuric acid. Now phosphate rock is a natural fertiliser; it breaks down and is released into the soil slowly. But the Americans didn't stay with that; they broke it down chemically to make it more soluble for faster release.

On top of the gradual build-up of phosphorus from the organics, the soluble super provided a flush of phosphoric tobacco, so that the leaf dried out a bright yellow. This achieved renown throughout the world as Virginian leaf. At first only small weights of super were needed in Virginia to produce the golden leaf, but as production extended to new areas, much heavier applications were required. (In growing tobacco to imitate the Virginian type, we found this was also the case in Victoria.)

MILO EXPOSED

WHEN I told Mr Slagg of the awful fright I got when I first smoked a cigarette of the Milo brand, he laughed heartily. He seemed not at all surprised. The Milo leaf, he thought, would have come from an area newly under cultivation; the soil would have required a proportionately bigger dose of superphosphate.

On our farm, he said, we needed to apply at least 500 pounds (227kg) an acre of this super that American growers were using. So we experimented and found we could produce the bright yellow cigarette-type leaf. As prices for cigarette leaf were much higher than for the dark leaf first produced, we set out to grow as much Virginian tobacco as we could.

Tobacco is one plant dramatically affected by phosphorus. Applying super to the soil changes the plant's whole structure: it makes it grow bigger, and the leaves turn a brilliant yellow when it reaches maturity.

The good years were 1928 to 1933, and to get the best crop we applied as much as 700 pounds (318kg) of fertiliser an acre. Some Ovens Valley growers outdid us by using up to 1,000 pounds (454kg) an acre. In this way our industry was dramatically transformed. By the 1930s "super" and Virginia leaf had become part of the farm economy in our valley. We were producing the right kind of leaf for American cigarettes. However, my attempt at sampling it was disconcerting. Ten or 15 seconds after inhaling I experienced the same sensation of weakness, loss of balance and pressure on the brain as I had in 1912 when smoking my first cigarette, the yellow-leaved Milo. By 1928 what I look back on fondly as "safe" tobacco had been ousted for good.

THE 1932 MOUSE PLAGUE

ONE night in July 1932, I was staying in a workman's hut on a friend's plant nursery at Burramine, near Yarrawonga, along the river Murray. The friend was Gordon Bruce, and I worked for him for five months on the basis of one week on and one week off. The hut had an iron roof 10 feet high measuring about 12 feet x 10 feet, and a stove against one wall for cooking. There was a mouse plague in the district and people had to take what measures they could.

Inside the hut Gordon had strung a wire across the room on which hung two bags of wheat, intended for planting. Soon after retiring for the night, I was confounded by a commotion of little squeaks. "Squeak, squeak, squeak," it went. I fumbled for the light, and switched it on. Little brown rodents were everywhere. They had climbed along the wire and chewed a hole in one of the bags. The mice were scurrying in and out of the bag; about 100 of them squeaking and fighting and battling to get a share of the wheat.

I took a piece of board and, as they emerged from the bag, I smacked them down. Twenty or so bit the dust. They were champion climbers. When I examined them I found cancer lesions on their ears, around the nose, on the tail and feet. Secondary growths were on all parts of the body — not a pretty sight.

I had seen Gordon in May planting the same kind of wheat, a variety called Olympic. He had used 40 bags stacked in the centre of a big open shed which had a mouse fence built around it. The mice had got in there too and had a picnic. Gordon's method was to sow with plenty of superphosphate. In May he had ploughed up the ground with great facility — using a six-furrows plough drawn by eight horses — and had a drill ready. I saw him put in 60 pounds of seed wheat per acre and 84 pounds of super. He would fill two bins of the drill: one with wheat and the other with super; the two would go into the ground together.

This would have given quite a boost of phosphorus to Gordon's soil. Not only was he exceeding the generally accepted load of half a hundredweight (55lbs or 25kg) an acre, but he was using the more soluble manufactured superphosphate in preference to the slow-release traditional rock phosphate fertiliser. So these mice had been living on this wheat grown with phosphorus in superabundance.

The seed hanging up in the hut in July was the only wheat left. Gordon's efforts of the previous year with favorable weather had produced a bumper harvest. Grass seeds also were abundant, and in these conditions the mice had bred up. So here they were, after several months of drought and with the cold weather coming on, starving and looking for shelter. Gordon Bruce looked at the mice and was astonished to see they were diseased.

RATS IN THE HAY

A DECADE later I saw the same thing again in rats. McNamara and Maroni, my neighbors at Eurobin during the war years, planted about 80 acres of oats and built three big stacks of hay made from oats.

The rats got into the haystacks and lived off the unthreshed, sheathed oats from December one year to May the next. The oats were sown with probably 70 to 80 pounds per acre of superphosphate (when 55 pounds of super would have supplied any soil deficiency).

I estimate 1,000 rats were killed by dogs, pitchforks and sticks in those months. A swag of rats that escaped came into my farm and ran wild. Several had at least one tumor on their tails, some sported half a dozen.

YELLOW DWARF

OWING to work pressures on our farm, we had begun to grow most of the vegetables for our own consumption in a few rows in ground fertilised for tobacco. Our household supplies of potatoes, tomatoes, pumpkins, marrows, rock melon and sweet corn were produced there alongside the tobacco crop. So if a higher than normal uptake of phosphorus in these plants found its way into my body via the vegetables I ate, this may well have amplified my reaction to smoking the yellow-leaf tobacco. But I did not make this connection at the time.

By the early 1930s our soils were saturated with super, and *yellow dwarf* had become a problem. In the late 1930s most Australian tobacco production was curtailed by disease, and World War II further restricted production. The shortfall was made up from imports of American leaf, mostly of the phosphorus-loaded yellow-leaf variety. At this time newspapers began to carry the first reports that cigarettes were to blame for lung cancer.

The crops of 1932 and 1933 were very profitable, despite the losses from a severe frost that hit the Ovens Valley on 21 March, 1933. But the first boom in tobacco growing was over. Our soils were exhausted. We couldn't make them produce on the same scale again. Another adverse effect of the heavy applications of phosphate to fields of crops was a marked increase in insect activity: flower beetles, leaf hoppers, sucking insects . . . more than I had ever seen before. Worst of all was a massive increase of the *Heliothis* grub, which took a special technique and much work to control.

The summer of 1933-34 was calamitous both in terms of a poor crop and of the state of my health. When more heavy amounts of super were applied in October 1933, all soils so treated went on strike. Apart from the paralysing viral growth known as *yellow dwarf* which had shown up in 1932, the crops were suffering from patches of *mosaic* virus and *bunchy top*, two diseases where the cell multiplication in the plant goes haywire (as in cancer). Gorgon-headed tomatoes and potatoes began appearing. In these years, there had been good falls of rain at planting time, and it was my belief that such rain allowed the soluble phosphorus to tie up any calcium so that it was not available to plants. In the furlough years, I made my living from sheep.

(I was able to grow a reasonable crop in 1938-39. This was achieved by reducing the amount of fertiliser and doing no cultivation or removal of weeds until they had taken out most of the phosphorus. Though it meant more trouble and expense, allowing the weeds to flourish paid dividends in terms of a healthy crop.)

DRAINED OF ENERGY

IN 1934 after five years of hard work in partnership, my health took a turn for the worse. I have always been keen on sports, and I was active in district tennis in my thirties. But my weekend game had begun to deteriorate. I felt drained of energy and strength. It was as though I had lost the stamina I had always relied upon and I was inclined at first to blame overwork. I decided to seek the opinion of my physician, Dr J.J. Kelly, in Wangaratta. His diagnosis was anaemia. To my surprise he advised not only rest but a tonic to pep me up — a bottle of A.B. Tonic Wine taken several times a week for three weeks. Twinges of gout in a big toe and arthritis in my right knee warned me that the cure might be as bad as the disease! And what was the disease? The first sign of it was the anaemia, which is a deficiency of red blood cells or their haemoglobin in the blood. But the underlying cause, I am now certain, was chronic leukemia, a form of cancer. In this disease white blood cells growing in the bone marrow proliferate out of control and fail to mature as agents of the body's immune system.

It is strange at times how cures are achieved. Late one evening there came a visitor to the house bringing literature. He asked if he could camp in the shade of the pine trees where there was a tap, and I agreed. He soon made it known he was a Seventh Day Adventist and I was naturally interested in his claim that one of the books he carried was the basis of a high standard of good health enjoyed by his sect. So, having bought this medical text, edited by a man named DuPain, I read all the relevant chapters. Disappointingly, this did little to increase my knowledge, until I noticed a two-page chart at the back of the book, and there came a glimmer of hope. It gave the chemical analysis of about 150 of our common foods. I thought I might be able to find some pattern in my recent misfortunes.

After some study it was clear I had been living on a group of foods with the highest phosphorus content of all. It became evident that for five years I had continually eaten foods that were naturally rich in that element or had been well fertilised with it and therefore could have been present in higher than normal concentration. As I had a small garden orchard at my father's place where there grew many fruits and some of the vegetables in the low-phosphorus category according to DuPain's table of common foods, I changed over at once.

In just two months on this diet, I was well on the road to recovery. My usual vigour had returned. I was confident, too, of having made a major discovery. If my diagnosis was correct, people suffering from leukemia could well benefit by applying the same dietary principles. The diet causing my sickness comprised cereal brans, bacon and eggs, meats, peas, nuts, coffee, vegetables from the tobacco paddock, and milk, butter and meats from pastures top-dressed with superphosphate.

OUT ON MY OWN

UNITL 1934 I had been working in partnership with my father and brother Eric. Brother Mervyn, meanwhile, was teaching at Port Melbourne and later built a successful career in journalism with *The Argus*. When Eric married that year, I decided to strike out on my own. At an auction sale of the Brady estate in 1918, my father had bought two sections, one in the name of my brother and one in my name. From boyhood, walnut culture had been part of my life and, as my section carried some 40 acres of deep, rich soil suitable for walnuts, I made plans to propagate trees for a grove. As cattle would destroy young trees, I chose to run sheep in conjunction with the grove.

Some 300 ewes were bought at first, and I made plans to subdivide the two big paddocks so that rotational grazing could be followed. Then when fencing began I found to my disgust that the property, apart from the area chosen for walnuts, had a poor soil above a big depth of clean river gravel. Wherever I attempted to sink a hole for a post, gravel made work slow and difficult. It took much longer to subdivide into paddocks than expected.

Having seen how my grand-parents and their family had thrived on the fruit and vegetables provided by their home orchard in those times of isolation and slow transport, and how necessary it was to grow my own in a natural way, I set to work in the winter of 1934 to fence off an acre and plant every kind of fruit tree that could be bought at the time. Though not as extensive as my grandfather's orchard, it has come to my relief at many times in life.

The rest of the good money made from tobacco in previous years I used to erect buildings, including a homestead. And to provide ample pasture for the ewes and lambs, I made a start top-dressing most of the flat area with superphosphate. Not for a moment did I realise what a unique soil formation it was and what singular trouble would follow.

PRIMED FOR EMERGENCY

MY sister Verna had married in 1930, very happily, and I was of a mind to as well if the right

Fred Mommsen and Verna Weston on their wedding day in 1930

person came along. At the local Christmas dance in 1934 I met a very attractive lass named Alma Greville and we seemed well suited to each other. She was on holiday in the valley and, as it turned out, was the first cousin of my best friend in school days. He had told me of her good looks. At once there was a bond of full trust and understanding between us, and we met up as often as possible. In the following Easter holidays, she invited me to her home. There I was disconcerted to learn that both her elderly parents had debilitating health problems. The father had cancer of the prostate while the mother had a bad case of diabetes.

My friend herself brought up the subject of health by handing me an article from the Women's Weekly headed, *Why some women are sterile.* She asked me, "What do you think of this?" The article, by a leading doctor, read like a layman's guide to choosing a fertile partner. The advice it gave was that you should assess the health of each parent in turn. Secondly, it advised assessing the health of the woman herself by her appearance, color, and general condition. It pointed out that the woman with no prospect of becoming pregnant was likely to have underdeveloped breasts. It said to get the condition of the breasts. (Of course the only way you could do that was when you danced with them. You could feel occasionally whether they were full-breasted or otherwise. I've known girls who've had virtually no breasts whatever — they were so small and limp that they were just lifeless.)

The article asked whether they suffered from any diseases or ailments, but also were their periods regular. You virtually had to be on pretty intimate terms with them by that time if you wanted to ask these questions. If their periods weren't regular, if they missed two or three periods during the year it indicated that their ovaries weren't working on schedule and that something was radically wrong.

One day I went across to this girl at Echuca and we were more or less open-minded about these things. She told me she hadn't had a period for three months. The most disconcerting thing this article in the *Women's Weekly* mentioned was a girl whose mother had been affected with diabetes. It stated that in nine cases out of 10 any child that came from a diabetic mother would be a girl. And in such a situation, if that girl left marriage till after she was 20 she was likely to be sterile. She would never produce any children.

I told her my reaction to the article later. It was a difficult situation but I still wanted to marry her. And if I had known as much as I knew two years later I should have seen the urgency and insisted that we married straight away. I realised as the relationship continued that she would probably inherit the same condition as her mother and that I could have a difficult wife to care for. So, rather than give up on the idea of marrying her — she would not consider such a union while her ailing parents needed her help and care — I bought some medical text books to prepare for any medical contingency.

Concern for her welfare was the motivation behind my thorough study of these books, just as the welfare of my sheep was paramount in my persevering in the study of chemistry. Once started, however, I was hooked. Thus I gained a broad knowledge of medicine, as well as food chemistry and dietetics, without ever acquiring a degree.

The author in 1937 after his North Eastern golf team won the coveted Leader Shield

When Alma's father died, I went to be with her in her grief. Alma and her mother decided to move to Melbourne where expert doctors were available and where she was to cook for their keep. By the time her mother died in 1943 I was sure I could give this girl a happy, healthy life in marriage. However, she married another man, a handsome airman. And as if to bear out the diabetes prediction, she has remained childless.

POLIO STRIKES

A YEAR or two after I met Alma there were serious outbreaks of infantile paralysis (polio) which caused great concern and apprehension in the district. As far as I know there has never been a satisfactory explanation forthcoming from doctors as to why such cases occur, so I think it is fitting that with hindsight I set out what happened to two of our neighbors.

In mid-October 1937, I called on one neighbor, James Mulholland, to see when he could come with his machine to thresh our maize crop. It was about sunset and I found him applying a four-gallon (18-litre) kerosene tin of superphosphate to the kitchen garden where their vegetable supply was grown. When he had finished the spreading, the ground was white, as if snow had fallen, and his two boys, Len and Reg, then dug up the plot and mixed the super into the soil. When I asked the reason for the heavy application, my neighbour enthused about the wonderful growth one could get by giving super to farm crops.

In April, 1938, the district was stunned to learn that the two sons of the family had gone down with polio; the eldest, Len, was dead and Reg was crippled. As far as I could learn, it was the practice of the young men to sit down after a hard day's work to a meal of vegetables from that garden, and meat, milk and butter from the farm's top-dressed pastures.

The second case of polio happened some years later, to the family of my brother Eric, but conditions were similar. It was Eric's practice to give his cow paddock an annual dressing of superphosphate. Both pasture and vegetable garden received too much super, and down went his eldest son, Adrian, with a withered leg.

FURTHER TROUBLE

THE Weston farm consists of 200 acres (80ha) of hill or terrace country and 150 acres of flat, gently undulating plain. The hill country has slate rock close to the surface, with little soil. The flat country has only a few inches of soil over a vast deposit of clean river gravel. The high annual rainfall of 45 inches soon leaches most mineral nutrients on this flat section down through the gravel, leaving the thin layer of topsoil as impoverished as any soil could be.

I was oblivious to how poor the soil was when, in 1935 after my recovery from anaemia/ leukemia, I stocked the flat section with 400 Corriedale sheep. I thought I could both boost the carrying capacity and make up for any deficiency in the pasture with fertiliser. That autumn I applied 70 pounds of super to the acre and the result was vigorous growth in clover. I applied the same again in 1936 and 1937 and there was further improvement. This encouraged me to use heavier dressings thereafter each autumn until 1939, when sick sheep showed things had gone radically wrong. The signs began appearing as early as the spring of 1938.

On a trip to Melbourne, I took along soil samples for analysis by the Department of Agriculture and while there consulted the sheep expert. After a lengthy discussion, he advised me to test out the problem by giving my sheep some powdered bone meal. Meanwhile, analyses by the Department of Agriculture showed the soil to be badly short of almost every element needed for pasture and animal and human nutrition. The ground was virtually devoid of calcium, sodium, magnesium, potassium and iron. This finding was confirmed in independent tests performed by Sharp and Howell, chemical analysts, of South Melbourne. Later tests also indicated an absence of trace elements.

But 1939, far from continuing to thrive on the luxuriant pasture, my previously healthy sheep were being struck down with cancer, arthritis and bacterial infections. They were a miserable sight: thin, emaciated, with a slightly humpy backline, the head held low and the ears droopy. Lambing percentages fell away and it was evident that many were sterile. I decided to cull 110 ewes as cast-for-age* and sell them. It could be said I gave them away. The dealer who bought them pastured them for six months on some rich river flats below Myrtleford where they made a rapid recovery and sold at a good price.

DISASTROUS ADVICE

THE soil tests I undertook on the advice of agricultural experts. The sheep adviser had suggested a test for calcium deficiency. The sheep

---

* cast-for-age sheep are those too old to produce lambs or wool; they have cast their teeth

man's idea was to supply the flock with a small amount of bone meal mixed with salt, in the ratio of 10 parts meal to one part salt. It was disastrous advice. The sheep who tried it did not improve. In fact, within half an hour the bone-meal lick had paralysed 23 ewes, all of whom rapidly died. Some managed to stagger only a few yards from the trough before dying. The vet diagnosed pulpy-kidney.

It seemed for the moment that calcium deficiency was not the problem. Nor was it obvious to me that phosphorus, which is necessary for growth, was over-supplied in the soil as I knew it to be in the ground fertilised for tobacco. The fact is that I had become accustomed each year to the cheerful sight of lush green pasture pushing up on the flats with the help of super and I didn't want to risk famine by withdrawing this feed to my sheep. So I decided to play it safe. Come autumn 1939, I spread another bag of super to the acre. This brought real trouble. The unsold sheep became even thinner, and examination of veins of the eyes showed lack of red blood cells. Normally they would be shorn in August and sold, but this year the shearers were late and so examination of the whole flock came did not come until the shearers arrived in November, by which time the sheep had been exposed to the full heat of the summer sun. Many sheep were found to have developed arthritis in the leg joints, and cancer lesions, mostly on the ears. One could say that the whole flock was suffering from anaemia.

Watching the sheep die like this reminded me of the rabbits suddenly paralysed by the baits I laid as a boy at the creek flat. Reflecting on this, it occurred to me that calcium is not the only active ingredient in bone meal: about half is phosphates. So phosphorus could be at work in sheep in the same way. When some old ewes had to be killed, only a small amount of thin, watery blood came from them. Even the lambs were small and thin, like a child with leukemia; the early anaemic signs had given way to this more serious condition. An abundance of superphosphate had led to arthritis, skin cancer, and anaemia. Here was cause and effect!

It dawned on me that the poverty of the soil could be turned to my advantage if I switched to an experimental approach. I would give the sheep mineral supplements. As the flock loved salt, a source of sodium lacking in the soil, I ordered two 200-pound bags of different varieties — one of sea salt from Geelong, another of common salt from Lake Charm in the Mallee. They preferred the sea salt with its trace elements.

The sheep would expect to find the salt in their trough. There were several of these small troughs scattered over the paddock. Next, to test their reaction to calcium, I placed a small pile of finely powdered limestone in the trough at the end opposite to the salt. This was also to their liking; they instinctively and regularly took a small dose, enough to satisfy their needs. When I was sure how much they needed, I mixed the two as one lick. I then introduced another mineral and began a new test. In this way it was possible to gauge both the amount and the type of chemical to supplement their feed from pasture.

CHEMICALS CAUSING ARTHRITIS

TO sum up, when I began the sheep-lick tests in the summer of 1939, my flock had been feeding on top-dressed pastures for five years and many sheep had developed arthritis. On being exposed to the sun past their sell-by date, cancer had also showed up. Certain elements had been applied to the soil and, in view of its confirmed barren nature, it was easy to evaluate action and reaction. Each application of super spread a smear of calcium sulphate as well as the soluble phosphate. After five years some 560 pounds (209kg) of calcium sulphate had been added to each acre and biological processes were making the components available to the plants. So my sheep had ended up getting too much phosphorus and more calcium and sulphur than normal. At the same time they had not been getting enough of other elements vital for metabolism and elimination.

I theorised that, since the body of the animal was apparently unable to excrete much of the continuous excess of phosphorus, it might store it up by combination with other elements around the bone ends. The joints were stiff and painful, just as you might expect if cells in the area were rapidly duplicating. This is consistent with medical textbook descriptions of arthritis. Further, I wondered whether what was driving the rapid and seemingly uncontrolled cell duplication around the joints might have something in common with cancer. A chemical link, phosphorus perhaps?

Besides mixing various nutrients to make a lick with common salt,

I decided to dissolve some of these minerals in the drinking water. In a short time the wary old ewes became reconciled to having their drinking water laced, and they grew cautiously adept at tasting and testing the water before drinking any quantity.

The first test sought to confirm the effect on the animals of absorbing excess phosphorus in the diet. (In this case it would be in their drink, but I reasoned that they were just as likely to get an overdose in the paddock from eating clover, since plants consist of something like 98 per cent water.) I dissolved 10 pounds (4.5kg) of super in about 40 gallons (180 litres) of water in the drinking trough.

This trial had some lethal but important results. Some old sheep would cautiously taste the liquid, shake their heads in disgust and walk away; but some thirsty sheep satisfied their needs and paid the penalty. In a few minutes the latter would lose all sense of balance, stagger about, and fall down, becoming paralysed just like the rabbits in the creek flat. Some died quickly; others remained paralysed for days or weeks. Those that died assumed a rigid posture — legs straight and head held hard back. Veterinary men diagnosed this condition as "scrapies". I was to see similar deaths in the 1970s at my brother-in-law's farm, Grevisfield, near Sunbury, when sheep drank from rock pools filled by rain after a top-dressing of the volcanic soil by aircraft.

I moved the helpless survivors to a small area of pasture that had never been top-dressed and tried to protect them from crows, which often kill by picking out the eyes. I diced windfall apples for them, which they ate readily enough. Nearby I placed a powdered mix, designed to neutralise phosphorus. Each morning these cripples were moved to fresh feed. They would just sit there for two or three weeks, eating what they could reach but incapable of moving to fresh feed. Then one morning I went out and found they had mysteriously recovered the use of their legs and were mobile again.

Late in 1939 we spread 11 tons of lime over 40 acres. This type of lime contained a small percentage of magnesium and potassium, and the sheep relished the pasture dressed with it. I placed licks in a number of small troughs. To try out an alternative source of phosphorus, we obtained a ton of finely powdered phosphate rock, which I used in small trials.

The plants were found to be healthier, as rain and biological agents released phosphorus slowly in natural balance. As with lime, the sheep showed an instinctive liking for this natural phosphate. With no new superphosphate being applied, and a regular supply of the other main nutrients available in licks, the sheep slowly but steadily improved.

THE WAR YEARS

THE war years were hard and grim. All able-bodied men were directed to the forces or war jobs, and I was left with little help on the farm, notably a couple of retired gents and two local girls available to help at harvest time. It was a case of working 10 or 12 hours a day seven days a week. To guarantee food supplies, the government allotted production targets and I had to produce 20 tons of tomatoes, 30 tons of potatoes and five tons of tobacco. Special quotas of super were allotted for use on such crops — and we used it all to meet our targets — but none was available for pasture. The tobacco I grew on eight to 10 acres, and the vegetables on five acres. Throughout the war I continued to use horses, enabling me to plough up to three acres a day with the double-furrow plough. (By contrast, the Furguson tractor which I bought just after the war allowed me to plough 10 acres a day.)

Just when I felt stretched to the limit by the demands on my time, a pack of cunning and ruthless enemies appeared on the scene to make my life a misery: dingoes. Majestic Mount Buffalo, visible in the distance from my farm, was declared a national park in 1907 and the wild dogs that hunted there were kept under control by a bounty. When the dingo trappers were taken off the job in the war years due to the manpower shortage, the dingoes bred up and put the sheep farmers in our district out of business. The dogs ripped and tore sheep to pieces. By 1943 there were only two of us left with sheep, Dick Rollason and myself. My farm was furthest away from the national park. He

Parks Victoria

Dingoes: cunning and ruthless foes

Tomatoes to help the war effort — two or three days' pulling bound
for the Rosella factory in Melbourne via rail, 1942

continued to run sheep because, like me, he had fairly well-netted
paddocks and could generally keep them out. Dingoes would follow the
cattle in from out on the Bogong High Plains, and even swim the river in
winter to get at the sheep. Once they got a taste, there was no stopping
them. One night my neighbor Ray Fleming lost 40 lambs, torn apart.

Dingoes would seldom attempt to get over a netting fence. There's
a hill behind my farm called Beehive Hill, with a supply of water from an
old mine. It ought to have been called called Dingo Hill because it was
there they liked to rest in comfort with plenty of nice icy-cold water to
drink. Most nights they would howl up in the hill, and always on a moonlit
night. You could imitate their baying and they'd answer you. The
moment the wombats burrowed under the netting and lifted it up, or a tree
fell over a fence, they were in. I gave them no quarter if they got in, and
shot them. They were a wary lot, especially the females, so to keep them
on their guard I would hang a lantern in the middle of the paddock where
the sheep were and fill it up to keep it burning all night. You had to keep
an ear out for the wild dogs at night, so the price of vigilance was much
broken sleep.

In the spring of 1942 I went down with arthritis, just as my sheep
had before the war. It hit me between the shoulders and was extremely

The tomato beds in 1943 and, below, tobacco and corn crops

painful. For days at a time I was confined to bed, unable to move. Often I had to be lifted to a sitting position in order to get out of bed; but once out of bed I obtained some relief by getting the warmth of the sun on my back and moving about to improve circulation.

I thought of the wild multiplication of cells I had seen in some of the plants on the farm. The common factor for animals and plants seemed to be that phosphorus, through superphosphate, was in surplus, other elements in shortage. Wherever phosphorus was added to the diet of the sheep, in pasture or in licks, it always led to kidney trouble, to paralysis, to arthritis, to leukemia, or finally to cancer. When other nutrient elements calcium, iron, sodium, magnesium or potassium were increased separately, they never caused cancer (although they could make animals uneasy). When the animals had free choice governed by instinct, they would soon indicate the quantity they could assimilate in the hungry soils of my farm.

Compared with the simple diet of the sheep, the human diet is a hundred times more variable and complex. I had been alert to the possible cause of arthritis before this, but now the excruciating pain gave me an urgent incentive to find a cure, and I set to work to study human nutrition.

FOOD CHARTS

THINKING it over I realised that better control of my own intake of phosphorus had to be the prime objective of any war on arthritis. (Arthritis is what I now regard as a non-malignant cancer variant having a certain chemical combination responsible for cell duplication around the joints).

The diet of sheep includes a wide range of grasses and herbs, on which chemical analysis was not available. With humans, the diet is much more complicated. But it was possible half a century ago to secure a chart setting out a reasonably accurate analysis of our main foodstuffs grown under normal conditions or processed under normal conditions and not unduly altered by chemical fertilisers or additives.

As mentioned above, I had bought a book on dietetics by DuPain in 1933 when my health was at a low ebb and it was a revelation to study the short section on the chemical composition of foods. I immediately changed my diet and soon regained my vigor. Here are the steps that led to that decision.

I was interested in knowing the combination of elements needed in the diet to maintain good health. To get an accurate picture, I selected 100 analyses from DuPain of our most common foodstuffs and averaged them. As the protein content is so variable, I did not take account of carbon, hydrogen and nitrogen. This left only the so-called inorganic constituents and phosphorus.

Provided a person ate a wide range of such foods, I reasoned, his elemental intake of nutrients would approximate this average. So the vital set of numbers is now tabulated as follows:

SET A

Ca	P	Fe	Mg	K	Na	Cl	S	Cu	Co	Zn	I
.063	.122	.0020	.050	.374	.072	.074	.078	(trace elements ->)			

where Ca=calcium, P=phosphorus, Fe=iron, Mg=magnesium, K=potassium, Na=sodium, Cl=chlorine, S=sulphur, Cu=copper, Co=cobalt, Zn=zinc, I=iodine.

The figures quoted above are percentages by weight. The phosphorus content of various foods can vary from as low as 0.015 in several up to 0.0709 in cocoa, 0.683 in cheese, and 0.525 in egg yolk. Grains, nuts and seeds also have a high phosphorus content.

I decided to compare this average group with 10 common foods rich in phosphorus, such as might make up the staple diet of a person or family to see how the average percentages worked out (Sct B). The foods were: porridge (oats), bacon and eggs, meats, bread, beans, macaroni, pork, rice, potatoes and tomatoes.

SET B

Ca	P	Fe	Mg	K	Na	Cl	S	Cu	Co	Zn	I
.034	.198	.0024	.041	.252	.090	.118	.156	(trace elements ->)			

It was also a simple task to select 10 other foods with a phosphorus content quite low in relation to other chemical nutrients:

SET C

Ca	P	Fe	Mg	K	Na	Cl	S	Cu	Co	Zn	I
.157	.103	.0014	.023	.443	.123	.146	.062	(trace elements ->)			

Combining the three sets:

Chemical	Ca	P	Fe	Mg	K	Na	Cl	S
Set B (10 common foods)	.034	.198	.0024	.041	.252	.090	.118	.156
Set A (100 foods average)	.063	.122	.0020	.050	.374	.072	.074	.078
Set C (anti-cancer foods)	.157	.103	.0014	.023	.443	.123	.146	.062

If you study the figures you will see clearly that, in a diet consisting largely of the said 10 foods (Set B), the phosphorus intake is up to 60 per cent above that in A. At the same time there is nearly a 50 per cent drop in calcium, a 20 per cent drop in magnesium, and a 33 per cent drop in potassium intake. It is possible to select a group of foods where the ratios are even worse, or again a group of foods that are in reverse.

When figures of Sets B and C are compared, the phosphorus intake in C is half, while calcium goes up nearly five-fold, potassium is nearly double, and sodium is up by one-third. The build-up of calcium, sodium and potassium is necessary, as I found in my experiments with sheep, to curb phosphoric activity.

Curbing phosphorus activity in my own diet was a case of selecting a diet comprising foods from Set C, which I have termed anti-cancer foods. This is the diet that cured my anaemia, as diagnosed by the doctor. The foods included carrots, spinach, pumpkin, cabbage, onions, beetroot and fruits predominantly grown in the orchard, where the natural fertiliser was sheep droppings. All these foods, and many others besides, are either naturally low in phosphorus or naturally rich in calcium, sodium, potassium or magnesium — the main elements which can attach to surplus phosphorus in the body and then flush it out of the body.

In 1934 I found that a nutrient intake like Set C comprising all our main food groups — carbohydrate, fats, proteins — did just that, with very positive effects on my health. So when arthritis struck me down in 1941, I revisited the food charts. And I was reminded there that mainstays like milk, butter, meat and bread were naturally phosphorus-rich. Even more so in 1941 when it was becoming commonplace for farmers to top-dress to excess the fields and pastures that produced them, and this extra load of phosphorus was entering the food chain.

A plant can easily absorb quantities of water-soluble fertilisers far above normal requirements, I knew from my studies, and there is no end to speculation as to the consequences. I also knew that constant use of super-soluble phosphatic fertilisers could skew the take-up of minerals and trace elements in food crops, producing mineral-poor foods. I wondered whether a better label for a revised average rating of these foods might be "phosphorus-dangerous". Therefore, I reasoned, even if I changed my diet to foods low in phosphorus, as in Set C, this might not be enough.

To cure my present condition, I needed to design a food supplement.

CANCER TAKES A HAND

ABOUT this time a friend named Mick Gardiner, who worked as a foreman for Urana Shire at Oaklands across the Murray in New South Wales, ran into trouble. In those days there were few bulldozers, front-end loaders or graders, and constant work with picks, shovels, axes or crowbars imposed great strain on the hands. A welt had developed on his left hand and become painful as it continued to enlarge. A doctor diagnosed cancer and advised radium treatment — supposed to be the cure-all at the time — but the treatment failed to check the growth. Doctors could not remove the growth surgically and decided to amputate the hand just above the wrist. Too late! As the growth extended along the arm, they again advised amputation, above the elbow. Again too late! The growth spread into shoulder and body and soon led to my friend's painful death.

I learned about my friend's untimely death and how he had died during a chance meeting with Mick Gardiner's son, and I was stunned. Normally, the son might have spared me the details, but he noticed that *my* left hand was bandaged and asked what was wrong. I told him of a lump that had developed there with constant farm work, covered up to cushion it against accidental impact. The parallels between Mick's fatal injury and my own alarmed me. A quick visit to Dr J.J. Kelly in Wangaratta confirmed my fears.

Dr Kelly carefully examined the lump for half a minute, and then said it was "a case for radium treatment or else." I asked what he meant by "or else". He said that if radium failed I would almost certainly lose my hand. This called for some hard thinking. I knew of two other people who had received the same treatment for cancer, yet all it seemed to do for them was to put the seal on their painful deaths. For me, radium treatment was ruled out. Yet what was the alternative?

My health had taken a turn for the worse. Compounding the turmoil of my dashed hopes for marriage and the crisis of the bandaged hand that would not heal came the cold of autumn. Only months before my 40th birthday I was becoming a cripple and going down with cancer like one of my poor cast-for-age Corriedale ewes 10 years before.

Looking back, I can see that this was a turning point in my life. In a special way I had been prepared and mentally conditioned to face this challenge.

DESIGNER CURE

AS children, my brothers and sister and I rarely suffered from illness. Partly I'm sure this had to do with the natural foods we ate and the healthy lifestyle of the farm in those days. But our mother also used traditional remedies to guard against colds. This included the regular administering of cod-liver oil and Epsom salts (magnesium sulphate). We would line up every Saturday morning to drink down our Epsom salts. Many people in the bush swore by them.

As magnesium is one of the elements I had identified as essential to balancing phosphorus, so Epsom salts were included as a mainstay in my experimental batch of mineral salts. Bicarbonate of soda was chosen for the "free" sodium ions it forms in solution, and sulphates of potassium and iron. It was a rather crude medication and I had to be my own "guinea pig".

The taste of the mineral salts, dissolved in spring water or stirred into the morning cup of tea, was not very pleasant, so I began to take a quarter-teaspoon of the powder in a glass of cold water with the juice of half a lemon. That made a pleasant enough drink. Alternatively I would sprinkle the mixture with sugar on my breakfast porridge. I trialled the mixture according to quantities and doses cautiously, and found my body could take a level teaspoon of the powder every day with no complications.

THE WONDER MIXTURE

THE food supplement was to double as a cure for arthritis and a cure for cancer. It was designed to counter or neutralise phosphorus within my body. I had settled on a diet of fruits and vegetables with a high calcium and low phosphorus content — which ruled out the staple of potatoes and tomatoes grown with the war ration of super. The minerals chosen for the food supplement contained the elements sodium, iodine and potassium, which the tests on my sheep had shown to be in short supply. These were the same minerals contained naturally in foods we normally ate.

The salts sodium bicarbonate, magnesium sulphate, potassium sulphate, iron sulphate and potassium iodide were weighed in defined proportions and then mixed and ground to a fine powder. At first, caution dictated that the quantity taken be small, to test the body's reaction, at one quarter of a teaspoon a day. From week to week I made adjustments to the mixture, increasing the dose of each main ingredient in turn to gauge its effect, before settling on the proportions published in my 1981 Australian and United Kingdom patents.

The sulphate group of salts served a double purpose. Being water-soluble, those of magnesium, potassium and iron were able to introduce these important alkali ions quickly into the blood. Having a germicidal action, as I know from my mother, the sulphates would keep bacteria at bay.

TURNAROUND

THE mixture was a success on all counts. First came relief from the torture of arthritis. There began a steady improvement within a few days, and in six months the pain was completely gone, a near miracle. In the years since there has been only one brief recurrence — in my right knee.

As for my hand, there was no visible improvement for about a month. Then a slight turnaround began. The first change that could be seen was a check in the roots or branches of the sarcoma-like growth* that had been spreading out into the palm. These roots slowly disappeared and healthy tissue took their place. The next phase brought a thrill of hope.

The blood, with its slight mixture of pus that had continually oozed from the growth began to dry up to a lump about an inch round. Slowly cracks, or what could be described as a separation between healthy and unhealthy tissue, appeared around the lump.

In time as healthy tissue grew, the lump was loosed from its bed to become more isolated and removable. Later it became possible to move it about, and I could see that a tough cord or ligament was still attached. Eventually, as this cord lengthened a little, it was possible to get in the points of a small scissors to snip the cord and remove the lump. The cord proved to be a combination of nerve and vein that had fed the growth and cutting the nerve brought a stab of pain like the removal of a nerve from a bad tooth. The slight hollow healed over but after 50 years the smooth scar is still visible.

I kept the lump for examination by Dr Kelly but, when I visited his consulting room soon after, I was surprised to learn that he had died — from cancer — about the time I had removed the growth in my hand. I have often wondered what his reaction would have been to the curing of the growth by this home-grown form of chemotherapy.

The mixture also protected me from infection. In fact, all septic conditions were eliminated. In all my life since, in spite of sustaining serious injuries and skin cuts or abrasions in farm accidents, I have never been worried by infections or put out of action by them. Colds and coughs also are things of the past, enabling me to go actively about my work on the farm with scarcely a day lost to illness.

And while there were occasions when I became a bit careless in taking the mixture, and even for a period of weeks deliberately went without it to test its efficacy, I stand by the value of taking regular weekly doses of the wonder mixture.   Nor did its development stand still. It has been constantly refined and improved in recent years to the point now where I estimate it is 10 times more powerful than when the formula went public in 1981.

Editor's note: A similar-based powder named *rhomanga* was Listed in 2000 by the TGA (Therapeutic Goods Administration) on the ARTG (Australian Register of Therapeutic Goods), marketed in tablet form by Health Research. A "food additive" alkaline-mineral powder was to follow.

* sarcomas are cancers of connective tissue, including bone and cartilage

PROGRESS?

WHILE the stress and restrictions of World War II brought me plenty of trouble, it also wrought dramatic changes on agriculture. Farmers were already hard-pressed by a severe shortage of labor, and high wages, and were working very long days to meet their production quotas. So there was much experimentation with mechanical aids to production and a general clamor for efficient methods to deal with pests. They had no wish to interfere with natural predators, of course. But as food and labor shortages in the later war years worsened, there was little resistance to the introduction of powerful toxic pesticides which could easily be applied by booms or aircraft.

These poisons were of two types: the chlorinated hydrocarbons such as lindane, DDT and dieldrin or aldrin; and, well after the war's end, the organo-phosphates such as Malathion, parathion and Gusathion. Looking back, it is a matter of amazement to me to see the naive way in which farmers accepted the introduction of these deadly sprays. Few realised the danger to the careless user or to the consumer of foods carrying residues.

Before 1944 insects such as Heliothis were efficiently controlled by a combination of natural predators and careful application of half a teaspoon of a 20:1 mixture of pollard and arsenate down the heart of the tobacco plant.

When the sprays became available, tobacco growers followed the lead given in the production of fruits and vegetables, and DDT came into general use on tobacco farms. Pests were killed off after a few applications of DDT and along with them went their predators — beneficial creatures such as birds, wasps, spiders, ants, dragonflies, lizards, frogs, centipedes and the preying mantises.

The highly mobile Heliothis and looper moths would flit away at the first whiff of DDT, and return as soon as a little fresh growth appeared in the heart of the tobacco plant. Without the usual predators to bother them, they laid eggs and produced plagues of progeny. It now became necessary to spray for the grubs 10 or 12 times a season to get a relatively undamaged crop. In this way, from organic sprays, cigarette tobacco received an extra load of phosphorus.

NEW PESTICIDES

S OON after the war started, a shortage of nicotine for sheep drenches developed. Some growers were directed to grow a variety of tobacco [*Nicotina rusticana*] which has a very high yield of nicotine. All through the war and after, the drench of bluestone and nicotine was the medication used to kill worms in sheep. Next came the pesticides, known as chlorinated hydrocarbons, which were devised by agricultural chemists to reduce insect damage to food crops and counter the labor shortage. To apply these sprays at minimum cost, boom sprays were invented. I well remember being invited to inspect the first one in action on a crop of tobacco near Myrtleford. By that time one had the choice of several pesticides — DDT, lindane, aldrin or dieldrin — for use in the boom sprays. When I arrived, David Milne started up the spray outfit and soon he was moving along the rows enveloped in a mist of DDT. Many growers made or bought similar booms.

DDT, otherwise known as Dichlorodiphenyltrichloroethane, was developed by a Swiss chemist, Dr Paul Müller, in the late 1930s. It was acknowledged as a carcinogen only in 1992. Farmers continued to use DDT into the 1970s even as the scientific evidence mounted of a link between DDT use and declining fertility in birds and mammals. Colonies of birds were dying out because their eggshells were too thin to be viable — DDT was interfering with calcium metabolism. The turning point came in 1969 when Australian researcher* Warwick Raymont made headlines by reporting the results of a World Health Organisation study: DDT had been found in human breast milk from all corners of the globe. The use of DDT and organochlorine pesticides was finally curbed by international agreement on maximum levels to be allowed in foods such as meat, grain and dairy products. Despite this, scientists admit that every living person on earth today carries molecules of Dr Müller's original 1930s experimental batch of DDT in their tissues.

---

* At the time Dr Raymont also warned of the potential of DDT to promote cancer and osteoporosis in humans. And, with 1.5 million tonnes of DDT estimated to have ended up in the world's oceans by 1968, he predicted a role for DDT in global warming — the increasing concentration of carbon dioxide in the atmosphere. Simply, the algae of the world's waters and oceans were responsible, by photosynthesis, for about two thirds of the world's oxygen supply. And the oxygen production of these algae, thanks to DDT, had fallen by up to a 85 per cent.

Chlorine is a very corrosive, irritating gas, and its addition to phosphorus in cigarette tobacco soon had lethal results. The way in which chlorine increased the figures of lung cancer raises the question as to its danger when added to water supplies. Although most municipalities in Victoria have been chlorinating their water for decades, others such as Myrtleford and Mt Beauty have fought its introduction and I believe would be none the worse without it. For public health there has to be a better means of making water safe, such as irradiation treatment (as used on the Mt Buffalo water supply).

It took authorities all over the world 15 to 20 years to realise DDT was a slow, deadly poison and to ban it, along with similar chemicals. This led to an even greater danger. The only alternative sprays likely to be effective were the organophosphates, and these have been in general use ever since without authorities realising *their* danger. The analogy that best describes this situation is "out of the frying pan into the fire". Cigarettes today give off so much phosphoric gases that I consider the smoker to be in similar danger to those who made up the first matches. The difference is that then it was known as phossey jaw, today it is lung and throat cancer.

A DEADLY MIST

A CALAMITY befell me in 1946, the first year of peace, as a result of a fruit inspector's visit to my home orchard. He advised me to eliminate thrip, aphids and jacids* with Malathion, a powerful water-soluble sulphur-containing organophosphoric insecticide. It is deadly to insects and kills on contact. The variety I used was called parathion. Gusathion has a slightly different formula but is just as lethal.

I had no idea what I was dealing with — there were no warnings on the label, and I was not wearing goggles when I used it. I have been paying for this ever since: I got the mist in my eyes. Parathion paralysed my ability to focus. Within a week I found I had to get glasses to read. I am left with only long-range vision, and it's thickened the pupils of my eyes and dulled my vision.

---

* A jacid is a silver-winged fly less than 1cm long and rather like a Rutherglen bug

I suppose I am in good company. I'm amazed at the number of people who wear spectacles these days. Go to any meeting and I'll guarantee nine out of 10 old people will be wearing glasses (or contact lenses), hopefully not from the same cause. Nowadays, on the land or off, it's hard to escape contact with lethal chemical pesticides containing phosphorus, and agricultural hormones.

Just for the record, hormones were developed for use in agriculture in the 1950s. Superphosphate was introduced to Australia at the turn of the century. Blackberries have been entrenched in Victoria since Baron von Mueller brought them here 160 years ago. That other bane of farmers, the thistle, is also exotic, and St John's Wort was introduced as an ornamental flower.

PARTNERS?

NEARLY a year after meeting Alma, the first girl proposed to, I was introduced to another attractive lass named Bonnie Bradley and we soon became friendly. We were both Catholic. She had come to teach school at Ovens. However, from our first meeting she made it plain that she already had a boyfriend and in due time expected a proposal of marriage from him. As our partners were 150 miles away, we sought to help each other along in the aftermath of those tough Depression years. I had a utility and used to take her on the odd trip through the mountains on Sundays. And we played tennis regularly. It was easy to see why, with her charming nature and good looks, she had been given the name "Bonnie".

However, I had no hopes beyond friendship with her, as my medical studies confirmed that she would prove to be sterile. Although strikingly tall and regal, when we first met she was pretty much skin and bone, with limp, lifeless breasts. Bonnie had the kind of youth in the Goulburn Valley where she lived on the poorest kinds of foods — bread and jam and cakes and so on, not the sorts of foods to build up her constitution and stamina. She was a terrible weak girl when I met up with her first. She didn't have the physical strength of a normal girl. Nevertheless over the next four years I could not help noticing a steady improvement in her general appearance.

The escape from the troubles of 1942 left me somewhat doubtful about the future and any prospect of marriage. To ensure my full recovery, I continued using the medication into 1944 when I enjoyed a feeling of well-being that I had never known before in life. This recovery made me speculate as to whether a similar, optimised mixture could benefit sheep.

Throughout the war years (1939-45) during which the usage of super was restricted and not available for top-dressing pasture, I had not a single case of cancer among 600 ewes, and this happy state of affairs continued for nearly 10 years while no superphosphate was applied to pasture. But an odd case of ear cancer and arthritis persisted. In the critical war years there was no opportunity to experiment with sheep.

During 1944 my teacher friend was transferred to a school on the seaboard near Portland,

Percy and Bonnie on their wedding day

some 400 miles away. By then her young man was no longer courting her. Bonnie and I kept in touch with the occasional letter. When I learned of the defection of the girl I had expected to marry, I became very mistrustful of women, and the rest of that year was a wasted one in terms of romantic attachments.

At Christmas,1944, Bonnie returned to visit her brother and I met up with her again. She really surprised me. Such a physique. The bracing sea air, good food and plenty of exercise had made a woman of her. Yes, I was forced to revise my former evaluation of her. We had always got along well together, and I became sure she would make a wonderful wife. The short of it is that Bonnie accepted my proposal and we were married when circumstances allowed in 1946.

SHATTERING NEWS

W E both wanted children to give fulfilment to our lives. When there was no sign of them by the end of 1948, she drove across to Albury to consult a doctor about why she had not become pregnant. The doctor examined her and diagnosed uterine cancer. He advised a hysterectomy.

This was shattering news to me. Having a family seemed hopeless, a delusion; life was suddenly empty. When I recovered from the shock, I took her to the two doctors at the clinic in Wangaratta, and they confirmed the first doctor's diagnosis. I was horrified by the prospect of a childless marriage and could not accept such a certainty if the operation were performed. Still hoping it was all a mistake, we went to Melbourne for a consultation at the Royal Women's Hospital. Two ladies' doctors, Dr Gleddell and Dr Hennessey (who were male and female respectively) gave the same opinion. And so, desperate to hear some dissenting voice, we went on to consult the man who was known as the leading gynaecologist in Melbourne, Dr Dick O'Sullivan. He was even more forthright in his verdict and suggested an operation at Mount St Evans Hospital during the following week. He then assisted us to make arrangements for the operation.

On the journey home I clung to the hope that the life-threatening growth could be arrested without such major surgery. I confided this to my wife. I told her of the ordeal I had survived in 1943 due to my wonder salts, whose formula derived from the sheep-lick trials. I told her how this medication had reversed the cancerous lump in my left hand. Bonnie herself needed little persuasion. She dreaded the operation. So it was agreed to give my home-grown medication a thorough trial before submitting to a hysterectomy. Back home, to give both of us confidence in the decision, I made up a lick for the sheep and had her watch. They were ravenous for it.

We cancelled the Melbourne arrangements and I set to work. All the study and medical knowledge that I had acquired to protect and ensure the good health of the first girlfriend were now called upon. The tumor in my wife's uterus by this time was a noticeable lump in her abdomen, and her periods had become very erratic. It seemed to me the medicine had to work commensurately better than for curing the lump on my hand. After hours of study of possible chemical combinations, I felt that the medication could be improved in several ways.

I altered the quantities of the main nutrients and added two trace elements to the mixture. Some of the chemicals were not stocked by local chemists and so I had to return to Melbourne for them. All were carefully weighed and blended. There was no grinder to powder the mixture, but I thought the crystals, being mainly sulphates, would dissolve in water.

In my ordeal, I had come to trust the action of lemon juice with the mixture. So again I added the powder in a level teaspoon to a tall glass of lemon and chilled water. If the water was too warm, the lemon juice would fizz violently and lose its value. Taken in chilled water, the mixture made a pleasant drink. Bonnie agreed to take a dose every second night at bed-time: at night because this gave the salts virtual control of her body for maximum effect, and every second night to prevent any excessive build-up of the chemicals within the body. (Too high a dose tends to cause constipation.)

Crucial to the effectiveness of the treatment — this mix of minerals in the role of food supplement — was the elimination from the diet of every food rich in phosphorus. Not to pay attention to this would be to feed the cancer. The safest foods in such a case are fruit and vegetables, and fortunately these were plentiful on the farm. Where possible I favored certain varieties of fruits and vegetables over others, according to the rating given in DuPain's food-composition charts.

As far as I can remember, the first doses of the medication were given in mid-September 1949. After a couple of weeks an improvement could be seen in her condition. There was no pain and the lump, which could easily be felt in her lower abdomen, began to shrink. After three or four months it had shrivelled to half its size. The powder seemed to kill it. The bulge was there without the lump now, just a flat shape. By the beginning of 1950, the improvement in her looks and health was plain to see.

HOPES DASHED

B UT as the year wore into March and April, I became alarmed. The lump, obviously, was growing again and Bonnie was repeatedly sick with dizziness and vomiting. This time there could be no holding back on the hysterectomy if that was to save her life. We made our decision. Dr Frederick Phillips in Wangaratta agreed to perform the operation the following day, but asked that an x-ray be taken in case of emergency. The doctor had seen the condition of my wife in 1949 and fully expected the operation had to come.

In a mood of utter dejection and frustration, we sat in the waiting room, waiting for the x-ray negative to be developed when we would know the worst. It was the longest hour I ever spent in my life as I had given up all hope of having children to carry on. Suddenly the door opened and Dr Phillips burst into the room with a very surprised look on his face, holding out the film for us to see. Almost shouting, he was saying, "Look at this; look at this." His tone of voice increased my shock and at first I thought my wife was doomed. When he saw that we had little idea of what the film conveyed, he pointed to a round growth of bone and announced, "Mrs Weston is pregnant!"

No words of mine could describe the emotion that followed this announcement: it took several minutes before dejection turned to elation. Before we left to return home, Dr Phillips advised us to make regular visits to him so there would be no complications during the pregnancy. He had seen the growth at its worst and believed it must complicate the birth. I have often wondered about his reaction when confronted with such a dramatic transformation in my wife. He never inquired as to whether I had any part in it but just seemed to assume that it was "an act of God" which just happened but doctors could not explain.

MORE DRAMA

D R PHILLIPS certainly gave all due care till the time of birth approached. Still fearful that the growth would make the birth awkward, he had a specialist from the Women's Hospital put on alert. As a further precaution, Bonnie moved into the maternity home beside the

Wangaratta hospital as D-day approached. Not all went according to plan, however. She entered the hospital but was unable to gain admittance to the labor room due to a prolonged and difficult birth that had priority. During the wait, her own contractions grew more intense and frequent and a nurse was called to assist. And so Bonnie delivered our son, Mike, then and there in the waiting room! He weighed nine pounds (4kg).

The arrival home of mother and son brought feelings of happy fulfilment and wonder at the miracle of the beginning of a new life. I had to keep a watchful eye on my wife as the growth and pregnancy had left her weak. Her sister, Noreen, a registered nursing sister, came to the rescue and helped look after mother and son for a couple of months. Even then, my wife found it impossible to breast-feed the big, hungry baby beyond three months. Michael was hungry as a horse, my goodness he was a hungry baby, and he had to be switched to bottle feeding. As the district had its share of polio victims and the first cot deaths were receiving plenty of publicity, when he was weaned we always gave him milk straight out of the cow, never pasteurised.

Relieved of the strain of breast feeding, my wife made a steady improvement in health. The doctor insisted on regular consultations as he feared a revival of the growth. There was never any sign of a regrowth and

Bonnie Weston and daughter Helen, 3 months. The children thrived on natural foods

a year later it came as no surprise to me that she was pregnant again. In due course, just 21 months after the first birth, our daughter Helen was born without any complications. But again my wife was weakened by the pregnancy and was unable to breast-feed beyond a couple of months. Nevertheless both children were to thrive on natural foods and on the fresh milk of our house cows. The milk was well balanced from the point of view that it had plenty of calcium and very little phosphorus due to the use of slow-release rock phosphate on the pasture. The children always had a wealth of fruit and fresh vegetables and both grew up healthy, strong and tough. To this day they have not had any serious sickness in life.

A TORRID INTERVIEW

SOME three months after Helen was born, I had to visit Melbourne. Among business calls was one to the Department of Agriculture in Parliament Place. When that call was over, and I was not far from Dr O'Sullivan's rooms at 70 Collins St, I decided in a spirit of devilment to pay him a visit. I had hoped to get the doctor's reaction, not so much to the news of the children as to the way that the growth, which stood in the way of our having children and which he had diagnosed, had been eliminated. It so happened that the doctor was busy trying to ease the pain of a woman patient dying of cancer when I called, as I learned from the nurse. The nurse showed me to the waiting room and told me she would tell the doctor of my presence. After I had been waiting about 20 minutes, the doctor entered the room in a grim, belligerent mood. He walked right up to me, raised his index finger to the level of my face and then let loose on me. "Look," he said, "if you are bringing your wife back to me in a dying condition, you deserve to be bloody well hung." Then followed a tirade of abuse that left my ears burning, because I had disregarded all his advice.

He stressed the urgent need to treat cancer in its early stages and threatened to report me to the health authorities for endangering the life of my wife. In his brusque, direct attack, he left me well scared for ignoring his diagnosis and advice. After a couple of minutes of this, he finally calmed down and casually inquired, "Well, how is Mrs Weston?"

Though notices of the birth of each child had been inserted in the daily newspapers, it was apparent that he did not know of their existence. After the blistering abuse and threats, I thought for a few seconds before replying, "My wife is still alive, but not so well after the birth of her second baby."

I will never forget the look of surprise and utter disbelief that showed on his face as the impact of such news hit him. After a few seconds' hesitation he walked to the door and demanded, "Nurse, bring me Mrs Weston's file." His nurse had already located this and she quickly handed it to him. He read it over and re-checked it for several minutes, then turned to me and said, "Well, I'm darned; in all my medical experience I have never known a woman in your wife's condition as she came to me to live 12 months, let alone bear two children." Then he shrugged his shoulders and said, "The inexplicable sometimes happens and the medical world would dearly love to know why." He then sought to find out if I could account for her

Mike and Helen Weston — strong, healthy and tough

cure, whether I knew of any treatment that had been given to her.

He had so scared me just before with his talk of legal action that I refused to make any further admission, and remained silent. It is something I regret to this day. That morning late in 1952 he had given his patient a sedative and was clearly exasperated at being unable to do anything effective for her. Later I was to learn from a mutual friend that the patient was the wife of a friend of his. Further, Dr O'Sullivan himself was in the early phases of his own battle with cancer, having been diagnosed with bowel cancer only weeks before. So the prospect of having soon to face a similar situation to that of the woman under his care would have weighed on his mind. And in fact cancer brought his life to an end some years later in spite of all the efforts of his medical colleagues.

I have often wondered whether things might have been different. When I entered his consulting room I had every intention of seeking his help in developing the treatment so discovered. It is ironic that, in trying to help me as I believe was the intention in his warnings, he frightened me out of giving him the one practical medication that could have saved his life. And not just *his* life. An opportunity was missed to get a breakthrough with the medical and health authorities, who in all the intervening years have been quick to ridicule my experiences and have chosen to ignore all approaches made to them.

A NEW ALARM

A T this time I had ceased to take any medication, nor had my wife taken any since her first pregnancy. Two or three years after our daughter was born, on a hot Sunday morning in 1954 while we were attending Mass at our church in the town of Bright, Bonnie fainted. After being carried out and revived, she was taken over the street to the district hospital where the local doctor was on his rounds. A hasty examination revealed an ominous lump in her left breast and we made a further trip to the clinic in Wangaratta. Again the diagnosis was alarming. Further consultation and x-ray investigation confirmed she had cancer and a mastectomy was advised. Confronted once more with the threat of major surgery, my wife agreed again to take my anti-cancer powder, whose use she had abandoned after discovering she was pregnant in early 1950.

Bonnie had a fearful dread of such an operation, so she readily agreed to proceed with another course of the medication that had preserved her life in 1949. She kept up the dose for four months, and in this time the lump slowly shrank, without any pain or soreness. When I first felt it, the lump was about an inch round, and rather hard. At the end of four months she appeared in much better health, and there was just a trace of it, but the doctors would not give her a clean bill of health until a biopsy was carried out. When this was done — they had a hard job to find it — there was no indication of malignancy, nor was there any sign later despite a careful watch being maintained for many years.

Relating all of this today, I am still amazed. The formula for the powder came together in such a timely fashion and proved so effective on each occasion that I felt, in a way, guided in my efforts. I generally prayed all the time for help on the farm. If you have any sensibility at all about nature and our life here, you just wonder at the infinite wisdom of it all. During her great trials Bonnie had a prayer book handy and every Sunday night before going to bed she would spend 20 minutes reading the Thirty-Day Prayer. If ever a prayer was answered it was that one.

PRECISE ADVICE

B ONNIE made many weekly visits to the clinic during her pregnancies for medical advice. She got used to consulting doctors and nurses. Their advice was given to her in such a precise and insistent way that she relied on it completely to the exclusion of my own. Then and in later years when she went to doctors she would never consult me about what was said. They were the experts. Consequently any criticism I ventured to make of her diet or way of life was just ignored. She took the mixture when she was in trouble because of her fear of operations.

If I talked about the benefits of low-phosphorus foods versus the shortcomings of the foods she and her sister had been brought up with, I could preach till I was blue in the face. In the finish she didn't seem to think it mattered. The older she got the more difficult she got. I can only blame her limited education. Despite being trained as a primary-school teacher — she taught children up to the sixth grade — Bonnie had an absolute inferiority complex about anything scientific, be it chemistry or physics, medical or otherwise. She couldn't talk about it; mentally she just couldn't take it in.

I would encourage her to prepare fresh vegetables as part of the evening meal, and fruit. Whenever there was fresh fruit available I always brought it in to her. I'd say, "You can't expect good health if you don't eat fresh fruit." She enjoyed a nice peach, or a pear, especially a pear. So I put it in those terms. No doubt my wife was influenced by Noreen, her strong-willed elder sister, who died after her, at Christmas 1995 of cancer of the kidneys. Noreen was resistant to changing the dietary habits of a lifetime and unwilling to step outside her familiar work world. She was a nurse by profession and placed her faith blindly in Melbourne's cancer-treatment institution, the Peter MacCallum Clinic. And do you think either her husband or I could make the slightest impression on her? Despite all the evidence that my treatment had cured her sister, she ignored my pleas about changing her diet and taking the powder, and unfortunately paid the penalty.

The birth of our second child had left Bonnie exhausted, and this no doubt brought on her second skirmish with cancer. This and certain dietary habits she had acquired. As a school teacher during the war years of food rationing, she would have experienced the standard and unvarying fare provided by the hotels where she boarded. Foods would have included eggs and bacon for breakfast and bully beef, potatoes and beans or carrots for the feature meal at night. The vegetables would have been grown, as I have pointed out, with excessive doses of fertiliser according to the quota production system then in place. Dinner would be topped off with a cup of coffee. In winter there would be a nightcap of cocoa or Milo drink and in summer a cold beer. An unrelieved diet of such foods and stimulants made from seeds and grains, a diet containing far too few minerals to neutralise and eliminate an army of phosphates, can be relied upon to run down the body's defences against disease. In the last years of her life my wife suffered from dizzy spells and coronary disease, for which she took prescription medicines, but saw no good reason to forsake her cup of cocoa before bed-time. She would not make the connection between what she took into her body at night and how she felt in the morning.

It is common for the medical profession to advise women that they need to have regular check-ups for breast cancer , etc, especially if they have a family history of breast cancer among female blood relatives. This is good advice as far as it goes, but it assumes certain families have a genetic disposition to cancer, which I think remains unproven. I believe much more emphasis needs to be placed on family eating habits, since the foods you grew up with are likely to form the basis of your diet today.

So far it has been my endeavor to keep the personal events in our lives in sequence and apart from other events and research which was related to our way of living. There was always some problem showing up with animals and plants on the farm that had a parallel in research being publicised by the media. The successful treatment of cancer on three occasions, besides equally good results on sheep, convinced me that I had the answer to the enigma, the solution to the puzzle that baffled science.

However, try as I might, all my efforts over many years by way of letter-writing, telephone calls and personal visits to influential people and organisations to seek official recognition of my discovery were rebuffed. Medical men in particular were dismissive. It is an understandable outlook, I suppose, considering that for more than 100 years across the globe the medical intelligentsia has failed to solve the riddle of cancer, with each new discovery being trumpeted, some having shown to be of benefit, but in the end results failing to justify their initial promise. So do you wonder than any claim for a cure for cancer was just treated with ridicule and derision? A few friends or relatives who were conversant with the perilous condition of my wife gave me some credit and respect, but most local people treated me as a crank. Only recently a neighbor died an awful death from facial cancer, always refusing to let me help him.

Also shy of the mixture was my brother Eric, a regular smoker for 50 years, who was battling cancer when he died at 87. He had given up smoking, which helped him, but died in the end of bronchitis and pneumonia. Eric had outlived his sons, Brendan and Adrian, who were killed in separate car accidents on the Ovens Highway about a decade apart within 3km of home, in each case from a seat-belt-induced whiplash injury.

For the record, our brother Mervyn died, prematurely, of peritonitis aged 67 due to a delay in receiving medical assistance. And our sister Verna, who never had much trouble at all, died in 1998 aged 95.

RECOVERY

IN telling of my marriage in 1946 and of the miraculous turnarounds in our early married life, I have omitted the unfolding parallel challenge of keeping my sheep healthy. I will return to that now.

After the war ended it was two or three years before farm supplies came on the open market and I was able to resume my experiments. Initially I was concerned to provide the sheep with more feed, so when superphosphate became available in 1948 at a reasonable price I resumed top-dressing with it. The sub-clover was well established over most of the property and was the only pasture plant the sheep had available as feed. Nor was it sprayed for insects.

The first application of super of 110 pounds (50kg) in 1948 produced better pasture growth than normal. Thus encouraged and convinced of a phosphate deficiency as a result of neglect during the war, I kept applying the same amount per acre each year for the next four years. The result was certainly lusher growth, but along with it came a plague of worms in the sheep, and a plague of sap-sucking insects in the pasture — earth mites, aphids, thrips, jacids, mealybugs. At the end of five years we had a plague of cancer lesions again coming up on the ears of the sheep. They were discovered at shearing time: not isolated cases but throughout the flock.

Cancer was verified by the vet, Mr Threlfall. All he could suggest was to amputate the ear — to get rid of the growth. But the tumor would grow again on the stump. We tried the knife perhaps 20 to 25 times in the first year. It was useless; the roots of the cancer extended far along the ear. We burnt the lesions off another 100 ears with a hot iron, searing it off. Searing meant more effective elimination of the growth.

Cancer lesions would sometimes appear on the nose and around the eyes, but mainly on the ears, where the small veins were most exposed to sunlight. By this time, in light of my experience with sheep in the early 1930s and my sheep-lick trials, I was blaming excess phosphorus in the pasture for the condition of my sheep. It had been absorbed by the animal's gut and passed into the blood and now in the capillaries close to the surface of the skin was interacting with ultraviolet radiation from the sun to produce the melanoma, or skin cancer. (It is the same condition which afflicts humans, and has the same cause.)

In sheep, the lesions would develop from this exposed section of a vein. These were dark with a tinge of red and would gradually envelop the whole ear, giving out pus and blood, which made the ear constantly sticky. And all the time the sheep would wag its ears against the flies. If a blowfly should lay eggs on the ear, maggots would feed and grow there and kill the sheep. It was a smelly damn business as well; you could smell it yards away, an unforgettably putrid smell of decayed flesh.

DEFICIENCIES

IN 1950 I realised I had to adopt different methods. The pH of the soil had been neutral before the applications of super. Now it was acid. We bought a rail truck of lime and I began to apply 11 tons of lime to correct the acid. (I did the pH tests myself.) The only possible explanation for our troubles was excess phosphorus. The calcium in the lime would combine with any excess phosphates in the soil. The lime, which I got from David Mitchell Estate, was half burnt, half slaked. It seemed to restore a natural balance to the feed.

I realised there were other deficiencies at the same time: sodium deficiency, from the way the sheep craved salt, and magnesium. Missing among the trace elements were copper, zinc and cobalt — cobalt being one of the essential elements in countering anaemic conditions and the subject of research relating to animals in our own Western Desert in Victoria. Rather than spreading these minerals in bulk, I decided to supply all these essential things for my animals in the form of a lick, as developed in my series of experiments before the war.

Animals cannot absorb and break down calcium compounds in any quantity, so I added calcium to the soil in bulk in the form of the finely powdered limestone. Initially I put a group of cast-for-age ewes on phosphorus-rich pasture. Again their ears soon began to show cancer lesions. I tried various licks and there was a definite check in the growth of lesions. When these ewes were shifted to poor natural pasture, the chemical lick began to shrivel the growths. Yet, although much reduced in size and no longer smelly and full of pus, the growths persisted unless surgically removed. If the sheep were shifted back to top-dressed pasture, the growths would flare up again.

ALTERNATIVES TO SUPER

A PART from the application of bulk lime (11 tons a year on 40 acres), I trialled alternatives to super such as lime-super mix and powdered phosphate rock. The latter is neutral and slow-acting, the phosphate being made available to the grasses by the action of rain and biological agents. And it has calcium to balance. The sheep in the field trials demonstrated a clear preference for pasture grown with it. There was no contest: I switched to powdered phosphate rock.

In a curious way the sheep instinctively sought out trace elements. During the years of top-dressing with super, they would avidly eat the bark off stringybark trees or unprotected chestnut trees, and when government chemists conducted tests it was found that the bark of both trees provided a minute trace of cobalt and possibly zinc.

This sparked my interest in trace elements, and one by one I tried out soluble forms of cobalt, molybdenum, zinc, boron and manganese in small quantities in sea-salt licks. I also tried copper, but the sheep rejected this. It was already in the pasture concentrated particularly in clover. (When copper was over-supplied it would cause jaundice in the sheep. Body fat would turn a deep yellow and the meat was not very palatable.)

Aluminium is generally thought of as a trace element in animals, but when available to excess can seriously impact on their health. In my sheep I had reason to believe it played a part in the development of anaemia. Again, this could be traced back to superphosphate. Super contains up to 25 per cent by weight of sulphur, and sulphur has a solvent action on aluminium in the soil, making excessive aluminium available to plants — and sheep.

ANIMAL INSTINCT

O NE has only to watch sheep grazing to marvel at how they can instinctively select a safe diet. Put them in a fresh pasture and they test the new growth by the smell. If that is right, and if that is good, they eat. Given a choice, they will avoid what is not good for them.

As supplies of seed became available after the war I sought to improve pastures by ploughing up about 20 acres and sowing a mixture of five clovers. As these demand a good supply of phosphorus for growth, I took the risk of putting 150 pounds (68kg) of super per acre with the seed. When these clovers had grown to provide good grazing, about 100 old ewes were put in there to freshen up before sale. I was surprised to see them walking about in this lush growth smelling it but refusing to eat. I left them there for two days, thinking they would settle in. When I returned they were standing at the gate, bleating to be let out. They had cleaned up all the feed around the edges but eat clovers they would not. Two had died from pulpy-kidney so, rather than risk losing more, I let the ewes out and left the clover pasture for hay.

Something similar happened to a friend near Avenel. When I called on him, he drew my attention to a paddock carrying a prolific growth of sub-clover which sheep would not eat and which caused bloat in cattle. Inquiry revealed that he had applied about a bag of super (180 pounds) per acre. The sheep had to be shifted when several died from pulpy-kidney. When sheep or even humans get more phosphorus in the diet than the kidneys can handle, such a diet can be lethal.

CONCLUSIVE TESTS ON SHEEP

W HILE a supply of lick had been kept up to my sheep and only 70 pounds of super per acre was being used, my flock had fared well. But I wanted to be sure that cancer could be caused and cured at will. So in 1954 the big flat with its thin cover of soil was given a heavy dressing of super and stocked up with older sheep from whom all lick was withdrawn. By shearing time in November many animals were beginning to show small cancer lesions on their ears.

These growths could best be described as melanoma, which gives an indication why this form afflicts humans. Just as a phosphorus-rich diet can saturate the bloodstream with that element and circulation in the capillary veins is poor, the sun's rays will cause the phosphorus to start burning out cell structure, which will continue to grow. When allowed to continue growing, a melanoma would slowly turn into the pussy bleeding sarcoma type, moving down the ear into the head.

The test in 1954 was too slow and prolonged. In 1955 a smaller test was speeded up by top-dressing a small area as spring growth started and stocking it with a score of cast-for-age ewes. It took only six weeks till cancer lesions began to grow. When it was obvious beyond all doubt, these sheep were switched to a paddock of poor natural grasses and given a supply of lick to two parts of salt. It took much longer to check the growth on ears than it took them to grow, for there was always a little phosphorus coming up in the feed to keep the cancer alive. The most satisfying feature of this test was that, when removed by either the knife or searing, there was seldom any more growth of the cancer. This quick result brought a great feeling of satisfaction.

Until this series of new experiments in the 1950s I was not convinced of the culpability of phosporus in causing so much havoc higher up the food chain. I could see that phosphorus was over-supplied in the soil and I knew it to be dangerous. I could now control its effects, but not totally eliminate them. I was concerned about the problems of cancers and exploding insect populations in the district, and pointed the finger at superphosphate, but officialdom was unmoved. I was one voice crying in a wilderness of ignorance.

ADJUSTING TO SUIT

FOR my sheep, a mineral supplement in sea salt was adjusted to meet prevailing conditions. There was already enough phosphorus in the soil for growth and any over-supply was kept under control with the lick, allowing the animals to ingest neutralising elements for full and balanced nutrition. These latter were mostly given in the form of sulphates. Results were excellent. The sulphur inhibited bacterial diseases and, with insufficient phosphorus to sponsor bacterial activity, we avoided diseases such as foot-abscess, foot rot, pink-eye, pisal rot and clostridiums. An era of trouble-free husbandry began.

The improvement in nutrition boosted both the quantity and quality of the wool clip. I took out patent rights to the formula and put a mineral mix for sheep on the market. The lick was by no means as successful in other districts. For example, where salt was present in soils or in the brackish water of some places, sheep would ignore the supplement or not take enough of it. Mixing the minerals with powdered molasses or crushed grain caused further trouble as batches of powdered molasses were found to be contaminated with salmonella, and this killed numbers of sheep. And surplus phosphorus in the crushed grain propagated and prolonged the very imbalance which the mineral supplement was designed to remedy. In the end, I was just content to look after my own flock.

EXPANSION

A S the decade of the 1950s neared an end, important decisions had to be made. Our children were growing up fast, so that a new, larger home was needed, together with an expanded source of income for their secondary schooling. In the autumn of 1957 I made a start on the comfortable home in which we now live, and I meanwhile kept a lookout for another property at a reasonable price. By means of the knowledge acquired in my experiments with sheep, I could see many more could be farmed without much work.

The opportunity to add to our holdings came in November 1959

The front garden of the farm-house with a view of Mount Buffalo

when 1200 acres were offered at Norong. Thereafter I was able to build up flock numbers to 3000. The lambs of both 1959 and 1960 were good, allowing all the young female sheep to be transferred to the new property to stock it lightly. The consequence was that when the Lands Department hormone blitz arrived, only the older ewes and house cows at Eurobin were lost.

DEVASTATION

DURING the last week of November 1960, I had gone across to Norong to deal with noxious weeds. I had to hoe and cut out Bathurst burr and Nogorra burr, and to mow Paterson's Curse. After a week of hard work I arrived home on the last Friday evening of the month, just as darkness was falling. My first act on arriving home was to check up on the orchard to ensure birds were not damaging the cherries and peaches ripening there.

The cherries were just ripe enough to eat, and as I was hungry for fruit which had not been available during the week, I ate my fill. I noted that some of the fruit had a queer taste. Next morning it was a case of being out before sunrise to scare off hungry birds. Again, although the fruits looked normal, they still had the queer taste. Soon all stone fruits in the grove such as peaches, plums, cherries and apricots, began to darken on the tree. Apples and pears also deteriorated but not as quickly.

Three days later it became obvious from dying weeds along the railway line that a spray outfit from the Lands Department had been spraying noxious weeds up along the Ovens Highway. This was confirmed by neighbors. The weeds — blackberries, briars, dogwood, St John's Wort and thistles — were spread over about two acres skirting road and rail outside the fence at the lower end of my property. The mist would have been carried into my property by the prevailing wind.

By then I had eaten enough cherries, misted by spray, to feel very uneasy and alarmed. At the first opportunity, I journeyed to Wangaratta to consult the fruit inspector. When I walked into the inspector's office, he had with him an English migrant from Cornwall. At the mention of "hormone spray" from me, he pricked up his ears. "Hormones!" he exclaimed, "That is why I am *here*." It appears that his family had a 50-

acre coastal vineyard in the south of England specialising in table grapes for the London market. Authorities had selected the estuary or delta at the mouth of his valley as a testing ground for the hormonal wcedicides, trying them out on the gorse and noxious weeds which flourished there. Prevailing winds had carried the mist up the valley to the vineyard and ruined it. So our visitor had sold up and come to investigate prospects for a new start in NE Victoria . . . and found us to be right up to date with technology. A rude welcome indeed.

The fruit inspector arranged to look over my orchard and thought the damage serious enough to bring in the senior fruit inspector from Melbourne. After looking over the blackened orchard, the latter said, "The damage is only superficial and I think the trees can be saved." He advised to spray and prune off damaged spears. Apparently he had little experience with hormone damage or he would not have given me that advice. No yields of fruit were obtained from the orchard that year as all fruit dropped off and dried to purple mummies instead of ripening in the usual way. I had to go to my father's old orchard for our fruit supply and thus luckily avoided massive hormone intake. At first I just did not appreciate the extent or serious nature of the damage to my farm. The drift had blown over most of my farm — pastures, orchard, vegetable garden, walnut grove and potato patch.

TRAPPED AGAIN

THE spray outfit came back again on the last Friday before Christmas in 1960. There was a strong thermal blowing up the valley and, as the prevailing wind blew across my farm, the spray mist was carried at random over parts of the farm. Fortunately my walnut grove was protected by the quarter-mile row of Oregon pine, but my home orchard, garden and pastures received a heavy dose. Again I was trapped, by eating peaches which had received some mist but carried no signs of damage at the time. After this lot, my house cows began to show signs that they were being affected by the spray. I began to wonder if the chemicals were being passed along in the milk and butter to my family. This second lot of spray caused so much damage between Myrtleford and Eurobin that a storm of public protest banned the mister.

I warned the Lands Department that my farm had suffered severe hormone damage and not to use the misting machine near it again. Next year they used a high-pressure spray unit to spread the hormones and this made a finer mist and almost as much drift as the mister. Again my farm suffered severe damage. There was so much damage to gardens, tobacco nurseries and crops right along the valley that the Lands Department were compelled by general protests to abandon the use of hormones. They had to revert again to the use of polyborchlorate, sodium chlorate or a new weedicide called Weedesol.

Quite by chance I met up with the crew of the sprayer at the end of November 1961, while they had their lunch in the shade of the liquidambar tree at my gateway. They told me they were using a "kill all" mixture on the noxious weeds. This was made up of gallon lots of both 2,4,5T and 2,4D mixed in 800 gallons of water: a double-strength mixture. In the days of the Vietnam War, where it was used as a jungle defoliant, this concoction became known world-wide as the Agent Orange herbicide.

I have a faded color photograph of the liquidambar tree taken by Dr J.W. Hunt, of Mildura, in autumn 1961, showing my children in the foreground. Almost immediately after the visit of the Lands Department mister, the foliage of the tree turned a brilliant purple and I would say became the most photographed tree in Australia. People stop to look; it makes such a contrast with the surrounding trees. Its leaves have turned purple at the beginning of February every year since, and remain so till they fall in May or June. The tree is still alive but only about 5 per cent functional. It has never grown an inch since, has no live bark on the trunk, and only gets its supply of nutrient matter up through the cambrian layer.

A MEDICAL CURIOSITY

EARLY in 1962 my health took a slow but sure downturn. Besides an endless irritation that shifted around to various parts of my body, my breasts swelled up so that they were as large as a woman's and filled with a milky liquid. This was accompanied by a gradual reduction in my strength and stamina. In that condition I went to Melbourne to consult the Health Department, who referred me to experts at the Parkville Medical

Institute. They gave me a full examination and admitted that they did not know how the hormone could be removed beyond slow, natural elimination.

My condition quickly reached a climax after my return home. The fluid built up in my breasts until the pressure became almost intolerable. Then began a peculiar and pronounced swelling of my scrotum accompanied by the shrivelling of my left testicle. (The right testical remains normal.) Alarmed by this, I visited the local doctor in Myrtleford, Dr Peter Broughton, who examined me and was amazed to see what appeared to be a small vein just under the skin connecting my left breast and scrotum. He took a photograph of this curious sight, and then to relieve my discomfort used a hollow needle attached to a rubber tube and plastic bag to drain fluid by gravity from the scrotum. He removed in this way up to a litre of fluid until my breasts were drained of it. But that was not the end of the affliction. Regular as night follows day, I have had to go to that doctor every five months for 37 years for removal of fluid caused by the hormones. He applies a local anesthetic and has fine-tuned the procedure so that the draining takes only minutes. Should I delay my five-month appointment and the fluid becomes over-supplied to the scrotum, it goes to my ankles.

The condition accompanying the problem of the lactating breasts, a constant feeling that something was moving about under my skin like some restless fungus or parasite, is described by doctors as peripheral neuropathy. And as fast as I applied a cream or liniment to it at one spot, the irritation would move to another. The constant stress and strain so weakened me that I feared my resistance to leukemia and cancer must have been quite low.

I decided to exploit the lessons learned earlier in life and follow a rigid diet low in phosphorus. On such a diet one avoids eggs, meats, and all foods derived from seeds, nuts or grains. The mainstays instead become vegetables and fruits. I found a magnificent variety of these foods available in season, and so many different flavor-filled ways to prepare them that all it took was a little imagination to make me forget the inconvenience. Nor was there any diminution of my energy from giving up the mainstays, and in fact I soon felt reinvigorated. I found I could wean myself off processed foods. For example, raw molasses has the best mineral analysis of all foods, and this replaced processed cane sugar in my new diet. And I did not miss common salt, which I wished to avoid as its chlorine content restricts the elimination of phosphorus. The new diet I supplemented twice a week with my powder, taken in chilled fruit juices — either of lemon, grape, or apple, with their vitamins and minerals present as a bonus. The powder helped by getting toxic matter out of the body. Phosphorus is mostly eliminated in the urine and I adopted the practice of drinking as much warm water as possible on arising or before breakfast each day.

A close watch on my wife and children revealed no serious upsets for them. Fortunately, during the danger years, the children were away at school.

STERILE EWES, 'PREGNANT' RAMS

NOT until the sheep were mustered for crutching in April 1962 was the full impact of the calamity on the farm evident. There were about 600 ewes and some wethers and rams. After the first run, my shearer, Jack Price of Strathmerton, remarked that all the ewes already crutched were in the same strange condition. Every one had the physical appearance of being within a week of lambing, with udders bursting with milk. Tests then showed they were not carrying lambs and were sterile. All ewes were in the same condition, but it was the wethers and rams that gave us the greatest cause for astonishment for they carried udders of milk like the ewes. In addition, the scrotums of the 15 rams were swollen up to three times normal size, and almost dragging on the ground.

When the group of 50 stud Corriedale ewes, bred off Stanbury rams, went over the board, all showed the same physical signs of sterility. Through eating the same hormone-misted pastures, our house cows went sterile and never produced another calf, while their physical appearance indicated they were soon to do so.

I saw much the same thing happen over at the Rutherglen Research Farm whose field day I attended for a number of years. There, in one trial, certain lambs had been injected with hormones to stimulate growth and fattening (to convince people that by injecting their animals they could grow bigger and better lambs). When people inspected the two groups of lambs, they were asked if they could indicate any improvement from the injection and distinguish between the groups. That was easy, but the surprise result was that the ewe lambs in the injected group looked heavily pregnant though not five months old. As in my sheep, the hormones had disordered their milk supply and distorted their genital appearance. I thought it a very poor application of science.

Our cows, like the ewes, developed indications of being pregnant and remained in that condition for months. Eventually we had to get rid of them as they repeatedly failed to get in calf. Two more cows were brought in and they got into trouble when fed windfall apples from the highway frontage which had received hormone drift and two sprayings of DDT. They were reduced to a very poor condition and finally died. After that, we bought our milk supply from a neighbor whose property was out of line of the drift.

When the lambing season ended three or four months after shearing, we had only 60 to 70 lambs out of the 600 ewes. One lamb was born with five legs and died at birth. Many other lambs were born dead or premature and very small, as if the ewe had been physically upset. But where the dose was heavy in the first two years, nearly all the ewes were rendered sterile. The large udder of milk which could not be passed on turned septic and there were several cases of black mastitis. Only one calf was ever born after the hormone drift, and it was dead on arrival.

ONUS OF PROOF

IN 1960 I wrote to hormone manufacturers, to the Department of Agriculture, and to analysts and scientific bodies about the cause of the damage. The answer they invariably gave was that it would be impossible to isolate the hormone. And in the absence of conclusive proof, I was advised not to take legal action.

I did brief solicitors on the damage and loss caused by the hormones, twice. But when the staff of the spray outfits were approached to submit evidence, they objected strongly. Even the government analysts were reluctant to make tests of damage, and averse to giving evidence against the Lands Department. So I had to bear all the loss and personal suffering for this irresponsible use of the chemicals by the authorities.

A most disturbing feature, arising from the drift, was that when received in small quantity, it twisted, contorted and deformed in varying degrees all kinds of fruit. On the windward side, drift caused a constriction and hardness, so that most fruits were lopsided. When 2,4D was sprayed on Patterson's Curse by the fence line near lemon trees when the fruit was very small, drift of the hormone caused the most monstrous deformities of lemons that I have ever seen. Apricots were all lopsided.

In spite of my efforts to restore them, it was evident after some four or five years' labor that most trees in my orchard were beyond recovery and more than 60 had to be grubbed out. Most of these were mature apple trees of many kinds that yielded 15 to 20 cases each. Even if some trees still yielded some fruit, most of it broke down near maturity and was unfit for use. One curious effect on fruit trees is that limbs lose their normal strength and become very droopy, even with a small load of fruit. Many limbs just break and fall to the ground.

It was perhaps fortunate for my family and self that the fruit was unusable on the two major years of drift. As little fruit reached maturity in later years, all sales had to be abandoned. Many years of my life have gone into creating the orchard and it seems that little can be done to redeem a tragic loss.

Of course, many of my neighbors also suffered heavy losses as a result of spray drift, as did the Forests Commission, which lost many of the 400 to 500 South African poplars (Deltoides) it had planted along the pine plantation between Myrtleford and Ovens. And subsequently, on the boundary of Porepunkah and Ovens a patch of 40 acres of young pines was sprayed with 2,4,5-T meant to kill blackberries, wattles and scrub. The central leaders being soft and sappy, the hormone either twisted or killed them. With no central header a pine tree is useless, and the area had to be bulldozed and replanted.

HIGHWAY HAVOC

HUGE, graceful eucalypts that once adorned the Ovens Highway are now riddled with dead limbs along most of its length, slowly dying 39 years after absorbing the deadly mist. The defoliant's most spectacular kill was a beautiful row of South African poplars growing between Myrtleford and Ovens. The glorious spectacle of the golden foliage of the poplars against the dark green of the pine plantations was soon lost to the valley. A few skeletons and sucker growth are all that remains.

After the end of the Vietnam War, many servicemen on their return home complained of ill health that had followed exposure to Agent Orange during the war. So great was the demand for a medical inquiry that authorities after much delay agreed to a meeting to be held in Wodonga. Having experienced some of the likely effects, I went across and gave both verbal and written evidence to support the veterans. At the close I was instructed to be ready to give detailed evidence to the medical judges, but this never happened and the claims of the veterans were treated as delusions.

Now, decades later, the debilitating effects are so pronounced after the hormones have wrought their slow, relentless damage that the government could ignore their claims for compensation no longer. Several veterans have come here to visit me. They were red raw with the constant irritation and scratching.

Vietnam veterans in general also have high levels of prostate cancer and the skin cancer melanoma, according to a government-commissioned study of 6,842 veterans and 3,629 of their children.* Their children (most aged between 20 and 40 years) had a significantly higher than expected prevalence of spina bifida and cleft lip/palate than the general population. Regretably also, the veterans' children had three times the general prevalence of suicides and deaths due to accidents or illness.

The havoc that artificial hormones are causing does not end with my story. Appendix D reviews the continuing "drug-induced vandalism of the female physiology" by the women's Pill.

EXPERIMENTS WITH VITAMINS

A GAIN and again since my return from the Parkville interview, some aspect that related to my malady would come to mind. At such times my medical books became invaluable references on subjects such as vitamins, amino acids and trace elements. I am an avid reader

---

*The Vietnam Veterans Validation Study 1998-1999 was commissioned by the Department of Veterans' Affairs and conducted by the AIHW

and one of the first effects of the hormone activity was a further deterioration in my ability to read small print. (Visitors to the farm may have noted my Sherlock Holmes-like reliance on a magnifying glass.) When the texts suggested that the intake of vitamin A, especially in the precursor beta-carotene form, could help maintain eye health, I bought a supply from the local chemist.

After a trial lasting several weeks, there was no improvement, so I gave up on the synthetic form and sought out a supply in live, natural food. I found beta-carotene abundant in certain deep-orange fruits, eg, cantaloupe, and in vegetables eaten raw, especially carrots, beet greens and cabbage, which brought about a welcome partial recovery.

Switching to all-natural vitamins, I also experienced renewed energy and vigor by increasing my intake of niacin (through eating more peanuts, potatoes and rice) and of the cobalt-charged "energiser" vitamin B12 (abundant in fresh milk, sea fish and lamb liver).

Nowadays chemists know more about the dynamics of herbs and vitamins and can explain why a particular vitamin taken in food, or as an infusion, works many times more effectively than a single substance made in the laboratory that is chemically identical. It is a question of synergy and natural balance.

When a vitamin is taken alone, it acts alone. When it is taken in food, or in combination in one of the newer supplements now available, its action is much more potent due to the presence of complementary substances working together in a delicate balance to enhance its effect. B-group vitamins are good examples of this. And it has been found that the dosage can be reduced in a properly balanced preparation.

For example, in some commercially available vitamin-B food supplements, all the B-group vitamins the body needs are synergistically balanced in a microdose. The vitamins can be retained in the body and be active for up to 72 hours before beginning to be excreted in the urine. (This compares with about 30 minutes for showing up in the urine with the traditional dosage of B-group vitamins.)

PROBLEMS LICKED

A N important fillip for my own recovery came at this time as a spin-
off from my efforts to customise a sheep lick for our new holdings.
For the sheep mixture I was guided to some extent by the stock
preparations put up by the Rawleigh or Watkins companies, who both had
quite a number of patent medicines also sold by travelling agents. I had
tried out these preparations on several occasions at various strengths but
had little to show beyond good tonic value for the expense. A study of the
analyses of these mixtures for stock showed a big percentage of
phosphates, which for sheep grazing on top-dressed pasture would prove
very detrimental.

To make up a suitable medication for my sheep proved more
difficult than expected. When so much calcium comes up in the food
supply and sheep had shown in trials that they did not like much calcium
in a lick, only a small percentage of gypsum, or slaked lime or powdered
limestone could be used, but which was most suitable? The base of any
lick had to be common salt (sodium chloride) so plenty of sodium was
available there. Potassium is present in plants in greater quantity than all
the other nutrient elements combined, and my sheep had shown that they
could tolerate a large amount of sulphate.

Tests on magnesium had shown it was chronically deficient in our
locality and that it could be used as the major component. To give the
mixture bulk and potency, I decided to add powdered sulphur to 20 per
cent by weight. The first test mix was limited to those five components,
no attempt being made at that time to evaluate trace elements as they were
very expensive when compared to the cost of the other elements.

A trial mix showed that my sheep gave their approval. Supplies of
salt and ingredients for the lick were bought and it was made up in
quantities of about 100 pounds (25kg). Several troughs were made up out
of red-gum blocks about a metre long and a third in diameter. These were
taken out into all paddocks where sheep grazed and the formula, mixed at
first with salt in the ratio of one to five, was put out for the sheep. They
were not very enthusiastic about it. It was much more to their liking when
the lick was changed to a ratio of one part salt to three parts other minerals
— the other-minerals portion comprising calcium sulphate 15 per cent,

magnesium sulphate 40 per cent, potassium sulphate 35 per cent, and iron sulphate 10 per cent.

The further work of developing a lick containing trace elements to maintain their health had an important spin-off in that it gave me pointers on improving the wonder mixture. I reasoned that the dosage of any trace element that a sheep would instinctively accept as beneficial would almost certainly be safe, and perhaps beneficial, for humans.

For these tests I bought small quantities of salts of a variety of trace elements from a wholesale chemist in Melbourne. The types chosen were mainly sulphates, for solubility. I drafted off 20 old ewes and put them in the paddock containing the long test trough. The trace mineral was mixed with common salt in the ratio of one part trace mineral to 8 parts common salt, and placed at one end of the trough. The sheeps' approval, or not, became known in minutes. At intervals of three days, I made tests with zinc and manganese, sulphur, cobalt, boron, iodine and molybdenum lying in the trough.

Considering that superphosphate contains gypsum, which automatically adds copper to the sheep's diet, as well as molybdenum, it was a matter of wonder to me that my sheep could discriminate in this way between the separate elements. But they did so, instinctively taking just enough for their needs. The minerals they liked I then added to their regular lick. It proved to be a powerful feed supplement. At shearing time the greatest benefit was evident — fleeces were 20 per cent heavier. I was able to make payments to reduce the mortgage and to reduce the amount of hard, physical work I did about the farm.

My next move was to work out the amounts of each element for an improved powder for my personal use, and to test it on myself. To my earlier formula I added minute amounts of the trace minerals liked by the sheep: cobaltous sulphate (to aid in the formation of human red blood cells), zinc sulphate (a tonic for the blood and stimulant for several bodily functions) and potassium iodide (energy regulation and growth), the iodine being in short supply in the soils of the district. After a month of taking the new formula twice a week I was confident that the hormones' activity was under control and life could go on, albeit at a level of strength and stamina below that of former years.

Fortunately, the new sheep lick greatly reduced my workload, as it gave complete nutrition and ensured almost full immunity against disease. It was no longer necessary to yard healthy sheep and vaccinate against disease. All bacterial diseases were reduced to odd cases, and fly strike, that most cruel and dreaded condition, became a rarity.

THE SILENT KILLER

IT has been called the silent killer because it strikes suddenly, usually in the quiet of the night when its victims are asleep. There is no warning of its coming, and no cry of distress or alarm when it attacks. Medical doctors, even after performing autopsies and thoroughly investigating the death scene, remain unable to explain how it can unexpectedly snuff out the lives of so many apparently healthy individuals.

I refer to Sudden Infant Death Syndrome (SIDS), or cot death, which in the developed world is now the leading killer of babies between one week and one year old, and especially of infants aged two to four months. It accounts for about two in every thousand babies born.

When a woman after months of pregnancy miscarries and delivers a child that is still-born, or else a baby prematurely, and so small and immature that it cannot long survive, this is cause enough for shock and anguish. But consider the family whose pride and joy — a lovely, happy and engaging child — is suddenly found dead in their midst. There is no end of the grief and regret.

SIDS has proved as elusive for the medical profession to nail in the latter half of the 20th century as those other prominent diseases, leukemia and cancer. And yes, it appeared on the scene after World War 2. Looking back over the first three decades of the century, I cannot recall hearing of a single cot death in this region (NE Victoria). Nor can I recall reading a newspaper report 60 or 70 years ago about cot deaths. No matter how babies were put to bed in the early days, whether on their backs, sides or tummies, such tragedies simply did not occur then in significant numbers, if at all.

Before commenting on the popularly believed multiple causes of cot deaths, I should like to throw some light on the mystery by revisiting a traumatic experience in modern times involving my sheep. When I began my solo farming enterprise in 1934, I stocked the farm with 300 ewes, increasing to 500. The years of heavy top-dressings in 1937-39 coincided with a large number of lambs being born dead. These dead lambs were also abnormally small. As described above, I had to compensate for my early carefree use of superphosphate, and the remedy was to give to my sheep licks of alkaline salts and to add tons of lime (containing calcium) to their pasture. It should be noted that both phosphorus and calcium are needed by the foetus for bone growth and other biochemical processes and a shortage of either produces miscarriages.

At different times lambs would be born whose mothers had perished or were unable to care for them, and these orphans had to be hand-reared. I fed them milk from our house cows. So nourishing and well-balanced for them was fresh milk from cows grazed on natural pasture that over the next 30 years or so I don't recall losing a single orphan lamb in my care. When our children were born and my wife reached the point where she could no longer breast-feed them, we had no hesitation in switching them over to fresh cows' milk from the bottle. Both children thrived on milk from natural pasture.

And what do I mean by *natural pasture*? Even a limited program of top-dressing with superphosphate, such as introduced on many farms since the 1950s, has an immediate impact on sheep, and most noticeably on lambs because "super" makes phosphorus super-available to clover and grasses. Fed on their mothers' phosphorus-rich milk, they can die with "rye-grass staggers" or "pulpy kidney". To guarantee a good and healthy milk supply for our children, I gave the cow paddock a dressing of (slow-release) powdered phosphate-rock between two dressings of lime.

We produced our own cows' milk until we lost our cows in the hormone blitz, and then bought from neighbors. And when the local farmers gave dairying away, we were forced to buy pasteurised milk from the nearest store or supermarket, like everybody else. This marked the end of fresh cows' milk and the beginning of trouble for hand-reared lambs — and human babies too, as I will illustrate.

The chief minerals found in milk are phosphorus and calcium. Other important minerals are present in trace amounts. Milk's original composition is determined by factors such as the age, health and constitution of the cow and the interval between milkings, as well as by the quality of pasture and the minerals available to it. Each dairy cow can pull a lot of different minerals out of the soil which need to be replaced. Yet on some properties farmers only bother to put back nitrogen, phosphorus and potassium. It is as if the mineral content of farm commodities did not matter, when clearly human health depends on it. The market certainly does not care whether the cows' pasture was fertilised organically or artificially, because a litre of milk is a litre of milk! What matters at the factory is the content of fat, protein and total solids. And what matters to the farmer is keeping up the supply. It is all highly automated.

I once paid a visit to our district butter factory and watched during pasteurisation of milk. The process involves clarified milk being heated to 75°C for 15 seconds to partially sterilize it and arrest fermentation, and it is then immediately cooled to around 3°C, ensuring a shelf life when properly refrigerated of about 14 days. I had the impression that some valuable calcium complexes that would normally be present in farm milk are unfortunately lost early on during filtration. Pasteurisation of milk is nowadays universally mandated by health authorities due to the potential of dairy farms to harbor bacteria harmful to humans. Nevertheless, milk from healthy cows is totally bacteria-free.

We have a wide range of milk brands and products nowadays competing on the shelves for the consumer dollar. This is mainly achieved through the wonders of reverse-osmosis membrane processes to concentrate the milk solids. There are skimmed and low-fat varieties, calcium "increased" and "extra protein" types modified and homogenised to please. This is creative processing and marketing at work. Because calcium in milk is the only mineral that can balance phosphorus, my shopping trolley favors calcium-enriched milk.

All dairy farmers like to raise good pastures in autumn months to ensure continuation of milk production throughout the winter. Little is left to chance. In Victoria, Australia's most dairy-intensive State, farmers are equipped with flood irrigation, as in the Goulburn Valley, or spray irrigation, as in the valleys of NE Victoria. Towards the end of March or early April, they give suitable areas on their farms a liberal dressing with super, and await the rains to stimulate growth. If rain does not fall, the irrigation schemes go to work. It is a routine that has been followed for decades. From analyses I made more than 60 years ago, I learned that such pastures can carry much more phosphorus than normal pasture. And in autumn or winter on certain days, according to the weather, the milk supply can be flush with a dangerous load of phosphorus.

It was during this critical time for phosporus uptake that the exasperating experience I want to relate occurred. It came in the dry autumn of 1983 over a period of eight to 10 weeks. My son, who has followed in the Weston farming tradition, brought me 28 orphan lambs to be fed and raised. As can occur in very dry conditions, the ewes had been starved for feed and had kicked the lambs out. Consequently the lambs were hungry. The only milk available was pasteurised, and I was having to buy 10 or 12 litres of it every few days. All went well for about three weeks, when the lambs began to die. Although they were well sheltered from cold or wind and had dry, warm straw for bedding, it was a shock every few days to find one curled up dead as I opened up the shelter for the morning feed. After all the prolonged feeding over the weeks and months, and even a final resort to prepared commercial feeds, only one of the 28 lambs survived. The contrast with the trouble-free early years of feeding with fresh milk, when it was almost unknown for orphan lambs to die, could not be greater. Try as I might, I can think of no other factor that could so affect the health of our lambs.

Which brings me back to human cot deaths. There is a remarkable similarity between the deaths of these lambs and the deaths of human babies of Sudden Infant Death Syndrome in the era of pasteurised milk.

The cause of babies' sudden deaths has been explained variously in terms of: (1) position in the cot, (2) breast-fed or bottle-fed, (3) use of special baby foods, (4) germ infections, (5) overheating or dehydration, (6) immature nervous system/ forgetting to breathe. I shall treat each in turn.

Firstly, when put face down on a soft pillow in a narrow cot, it is possible that a baby can smother. A baby placed on its back in such a cot can have difficulty disposing of wind, a source of discomfort and danger. My children were bedded in a 4' x 3' cot on a fairly firm mattress and placed on their right side to reduce heart strain and with a warm covering that allowed free movement. There was never any trouble.

Secondly, it is not often that a breast-fed baby will die of SIDS. Human breast milk is naturally designed for human infants, and not calves, and provides the best possible nourishment for the developing human being in the early months. It has a lower mineral content than either cow or goats' milk. Nevertheless, SIDS is possible with breastfed milk and depends on the diet of the mother. For instance, if the mother of a young baby ate a breakfast of All-Bran™ or Corn Flakes™, pasteurised milk, bacon and egg, toast spread with margarine, along with a cup of coffee, there could be trouble ahead, especially if this were followed by a midday meal similarly rich in phosphorus and lacking balancing minerals. By evening the breast-fed baby could well have received an overload of phosphorus from the mother's milk, possibly even enough to paralyse its heart or breathing muscles. The actual mode of death, of course, leaves no discernible sign. It can only be discovered by investigation of the chemistry of the food taken before death.

Infants may be bottle-fed either fresh milk (from cow or goat) or pasteurised milk — although these days there is little opportunity to buy unpasteurised. Fresh milk from natural pasture should present no hazard . . . not like the risk posed from pasture dressed with superphosphate. I have already pointed out that dairy products involving super in the food chain can also bring on polio, which usually comes at a later age. I have related how in the autumn of 1938 the two sons of our neighbor were stricken in one night with polio, and that from what I saw of his farm management dairy products were suspect. So much so that when I saw my brother repeatedly give his cow paddock annual dressings of super, I warned him of the danger to his children. Sure enough, one of his boys suffered a severe attack of polio. Knowing the culprit to be phosphorus, I think I can suggest just the medication to counter an attack of polio soon after its onset.

In summary, then, copious drinks of manufactured fresh milk delivered by bottle before bedtime, with or without the help of a diet of phosphorus-rich breakfast foods and commercial vegetables, can put any infant at risk. It can also cause the paralysis of asthma, a disease now afflicting some 600,000 Australians, from the same cause. Unfortunately, one has no way of knowing the source of the milk: that is, whether the farm it came from used super-soluble superphosphate as fertiliser or the relatively safe rock phosphate with enough calcium in the soil to balance. The best kinds of vegetables are the ones you grow yourself and eat fresh or buy from organic farmers; they also taste the best. Having examined all the baby foods obtainable at our local chemists and supermarkets, I must say they contain some very questionable additives. On my ranking of foods according to mineral balance, they come in at 2 on the lower end of the scale. The fact also that many of these commercial foods are sterile and dead does not help a baby as live foods can do. This covers the use of special baby foods. Earlier I warned that phosphorus can stimulate germ activity, and the dairy industry is a good example. Dairy herds are notorious for outbreaks of infectious disease, notably mastitis, three-day sickness, and milk fever, and sanitation is enforced to protect them. To protect humans, we have pasteurisation of dairy products, and then cleanliness and sterilisation is practised, from milk machine to bulk tanker through to the processing plant to packaging, all the way down the chain to storage and distribution to shops. The mother of a young baby must be just as careful. The slightest lapse in home hygiene can place her baby in peril. While a cold or germ infection can noticeably weaken a baby over a number of days, I believe it is the milk supply about which one needs to be most vigilant.

It could be of interest to the reader to know that right through my infancy from1903, when no refrigeration was possible, till some 60 years later, our household milk supply came from cows milked twice daily. I can never recall being in trouble with the milk supply, and the only sanitation employed was to sterilise every dairy utensil with boiling water.

On the fifth point, concerning over-heating or dehydration, most babies can cry out and attract attention. But when half-sedated by a phosphorus-rich milk, they cannot warn you they are in trouble. Every year hundreds of cows die from a condition known as bloat, which results when cows graze on certain top-dressed pasture plants. Their digestive apparatus becomes paralysed and they are unable to belch out the gases of fermentation in the rumen. Gas pressure can be so great that heart and lungs cannot function, and the cows die just as quietly as a baby in cot death. (For a fuller treatment of bloat in cattle, see Appendix D.)

Given more rich milk than it can digest can put a baby into acute distress. My wife found it difficult to breast-feed her babies for more than three months, when bottle-feeding began. We were careful to "burp" and exercise the babies to ensure they were comfortable before being cotted for the night.

The issue of an immature nervous system causing a newborn baby to suddenly stop breathing and expire misses the point about the diet and phosphorus-induced paralysis. It could affect any baby, but I haven't heard of any such cases (apart from premature babies) before the use of superphosphate became general. Other modern risk factors suggested include maternal smoking (again, phosphorus-related!) and drug use (certainly!), poor prenatal care (yes) and low birth weight (like some of my poor lambs born in the years 1937-39).

MEDICAL MICAWBERS

MEDICAL researchers have an amazing capacity to stay focused on their own work. From time to time as the years fled by after 1962 there would be an article in the daily paper or a talk on the radio about some new discovery relating to cancer research. If an address were given by one of these eternal optimists and it seemed to me the professor or learned researcher were on the wrong track, I would write to him and tell him so.

This proved futile. Every approach was either ignored or the recipient showed no interest in investigating the evidence that I offered to supply. And any letter of comment that I wrote in long-hand to the editor of a newspaper was invariably ignored. They would never allow a comment from a reader whose signature did not bear at least the letters MD to back it up. Similarly a series of letters written to the Anti-Cancer Council produced no fruits, though usually they did me the courtesy of a reply.

I kept this up for 10 years. Then one day I was visiting Melbourne and happened to be near the Department of Health in Queen Street with an hour to spare. So I ventured in to see if the minister would grant me an interview. I briefed the clerk in the inquiry office, who rang the minister's office. Down came a member of his staff to meet me. This courteous man

The farm workhorse, the Massey-Ferguson tractor, gets a check-up in earlier
days from young Michael Weston

guided me along corridors and around corners until I was sure I was about
to enter the minister's office. Instead I found myself being suddenly
ushered out into Queen Street with the parting remark that the minister
was much too busy to discuss such matters with a retired farmer!

A CLOSE CALL

IN 1967 our wool clip amounted to 118 bales and it looked as if all
financial commitments could be met.   But wool prices took a
disastrous tumble that year and, instead of recovering more than $40,000
for the clip, we got back only $17,000.   The next few years were very
hard. In the periods between drought and flood most people imagine that
farmers live pretty well, but I can tell you that at that time we were
working for nothing. The low prices for both wool and sheep continued
into 1972, when my life went close to ending.

Early on the morning of 2nd November, 1972, I set out on my

Ferguson tractor to prepare 10 acres for a seasonal crop. All went well till about 9am when heavy clouds loomed up and a rainstorm threatened. Within 100 metres from the finish, heavy rain began to fall. The clod crusher began to gather up sticky wet soil and about 20 metres before the end of the land the tractor suddenly stopped under the heavy load, though the engine continued to run.

It seemed that the main drive shaft or an axle had broken, so I jumped off to investigate the power takeoff. Finding that working, I went to remount to test the gears, but as soon as my foot hit the footplate, the clutch which had been slipping suddenly grabbed, causing the tractor to jump forward. The bigger wheel of the tractor caught me off balance, knocked me down and passed over my chest and shoulders. By a miracle, the tractor stalled and stopped before the clod crusher ended my life.

The events of the next few hours and weeks will be described in some detail to let the reader know what a grim ordeal the human body can endure. It can only be a matter of wonder to the reader that this story was ever told. The large rear wheel of the tractor passed over my body on a slight angle, crushing the ribs on the left side on to heart and lungs, bruised my right shoulder and arm, then grazed my right ear and head. Fortunately, I retained the power to think, allowing me to instinctively react in the right way. My heart was struggling to beat against the broken ribs, so there was no option but to take a deep breath, no matter how it hurt, and force the broken ribs off the heart.

By sliding my right arm across my body and under the left trouser brace, it was possible to hold the ribs back in position. By this time the cold rain was pelting down so I was soon wet through and covered in mud. By gripping the chain from the draw bar to the clod crusher with my left hand I had just enough strength to pull myself to a sitting position and then struggle to my feet. Then only did I realise that there was no feeling beyond "pins and needles" in either hands or feet, while there was an injury to my spine at the base of my neck that could be felt.

STRANDED

STANDING beside the tractor for at least two minutes to sum up the situation, it was clear that no help was available as Bonnie was away. It was a case of trying to struggle back to the house some 300 metres away. There was a fence close by and somehow I managed to get across to it. By clinging to the fence to maintain balance, it took me over an hour to stagger back to the house. There I was so cold and exhausted that I never thought of phoning for help. The wet clothes had to be painfully removed and I climbed into bed naked to go into a coma.

It was 5pm — seven hours after the accident — when agonising pain brought me back to my senses. As both children and my wife were on holiday, it was a case of crawling out to the phone to ring my brother. By 6pm an ambulance had picked me up and gently delivered me to Wangaratta hospital. By this time my body from waist to neck was so black from massive blood clotting and so paralysed that the doctor on duty decided it was too dangerous to do anything to help. A blood clot had only to move to the heart or the brain to end my life.

For a week, pillows were used to hold me in a sitting position with hands locked in front of the solar plexus while breathing was reduced to about 10 per cent of normal as any rib movement brought extreme pain. Likewise any inclination to cough, sneeze or even laugh had to be stifled as they soon taught that any movement of the broken ribs meant more pain. This was so intense that there was no sleep for two nights. And every four or five hours nurses would change my singlet or pyjamas as they became saturated by sweat. Doctors did not dare to move blood clots and I had a feeling that my life here was nearing the end.

As the spasms of pain racked my body and the profuse nervous sweating stained my clothes, I recalled in vivid detail the crucifixion and resurrection of Christ that I had studied at Xavier College, and I became convinced of the further authenticity of his burial cloth, the Shroud of Turin, imprinted with the wounds of his suffering and preserved down the centuries. People have long thought this ancient linen cloth to be genuine because the stains on the Shroud closely match up with the wounds from Christ's flogging and crucifixion and could not have been painted on from any artist's perspective. The negative image on the cloth most closely resembles a long-lasting contact-photograph.

As the result of the nurses having taken off my saturated clothes and parked me between sheets, I could see imprinted on the sheets a faint picture of my own body, from my neck down to my hips. It was most pronounced around the wounded areas where the sweat was bringing out a trace of blood. These impregnations were not made by dried blood cells flaking off a dead man but rather by secretions from a wounded body sweating profusely. It made me think that when Christ came to life the nervous sweat would come out and make a perfect imprint of the whole body, both front and back on the burial cloth. Here for me was verification of the resurrection of Christ in the internal evidence of the Shroud.

HOME TREATMENT

MY sojourn in hospital ended when a 34-year-old man was brought in with a serious heart condition and doctors soon indicated that they could help him while they could do nothing for a 69-year-old who seemed doomed to die. It was a great relief to get home as my condition was getting really desperate: my lungs were filling up with fluid and pneumonia loomed.

It was at this stage that my knowledge of diet and medication came to the rescue. A diet of chosen foods was kept to minimum needs while medication was stepped up to counter sore infections as the accident had caused skin abrasions which showed signs of Golden Staph. So it was a very difficult time with so many maladies to beat.

The lung congestion was beaten by putting pillows high on a single bed and hanging over the side of the pile, allowing gravity to drain fluid and mucus from my lungs. A pillow on a 44-gallon (200-litre) drum was even more effective.

And a university textbook, *Guyton's Book of Medical Physiology*, which my daughter obtained for me, had useful information which helped get me through the danger period. While the blood clotting was slowly clearing up without any complications — thanks to the powder — the sleepy hands and feet were the source of great worry. My wife always assisted me to keep erect when some gentle exercise was taken every day to help recovery.

Six weeks passed before all signs of possible blood clotting and muscle soreness disappeared, yet doctors were wary of treating my paralysed limbs. As the soreness in my arms lessened, it became clear that the third and little fingers in both hands had become lifeless. The nerves which enable them to function had been guillotined by pressure on the shoulder blades as the tractor passed over them.

CHIROPRACTIC

TWO months after the accident I was taken on a visit to Wangaratta for examination by a chiropractor, Dr Leo Maguire. I had met him playing golf. He advised x-rays from several angles to spot the cause of the paralysis. The first thing obvious was that the four segments of my spine between my shoulders were calcified together. On his inquiry about arthritis, I told him of my bout in 1942-43 when I spent nine months in trouble. Just on top of this combination, the x-ray revealed a subluxation: two segments that had been forced slightly out of alignment and were pinching the spinal cord. He said a little more pressure or pinching would have severed it, either killing me or making me a quadriplegic. After fingering the dislocation for a couple of minutes, he told me to come back a week later when he thought he might have a technique to get the segments into line without complications.

On my next visit he first warmed up the area around the dislocation to relax muscles, asked me to bend my head forward as far as possible and then, placing the edge of his left hand on the displaced segment, he succeeded on the second, heavier blow with his right fist in bringing this segment back into place. I could feel pins and needles in my left hand as nerves again tingled with life. A month later I was as fit and well as one could expect at 69. While my ribs healed slightly out of line, the third and little fingers of my right hand are still paralysed but give little handicap.

NEW DIRECTIONS

I AM pleased to say that not just my immediate family but a wide circle of relatives and friends were relieved to see me survive the tractor trauma, when it was my funeral they had been expecting. Now, 27 years later, I am still going strong and hoping to be able to serve others for a few more years to come.

When I had fully recovered, Les Goldsworthy and his wife came to visit me and passed on an invitation from Dr Maurice Finkel*, an American doctor practising in Melbourne, that changed the rest of my life. This was to address a meeting of the International Association of Cancer Victors and Friends (IACVF) in Melbourne about my approach to beating cancer. I accepted and was given an excellent hearing by about 50 people who came from all walks of life and for whom my story of family cures and the epidemic of cancer among my sheep had the ring of truth. Some asked me to supply the anti-cancer powder, and encouraged me to patent the formula.

So I determined to put the details on the public record in the form of a patent and began to publicise the nature of cancer and its effective cure to a wider public.   This has produced a steady stream of correspondence, visitors and phone calls from people seeking help from Australia and abroad.   And I am pleased to say many of them have been helped, as a selection of their testimonies in a later chapter shows. I joined up as an active member of the IACVF and went on to give talks and lectures and to take part in some rewarding discussions in Melbourne, in Tasmania, and closer to home.

If my anti-cancer powder had worked only on myself and on my scientifically uncultivated wife, then perhaps people could say it was just faith healing and therefore inaccessible to them, or a fluke of nature. But what gave me the conviction that I had made a great discovery was that it worked on other people too.

When I began to speak in public about the discovery, people approached me and implored me to help their friends and relatives who were in trouble with cancer. But usually such cancer sufferers had already exhausted all avenues of orthodox treatment. This is not to deny that orthodox medicine has made some progress in stemming cancer in its early stages. "Early detection can mean successful treatment," is the authorities' catch cry, although such intervention hardly ever goes to the root of the problem, and the cancer will invariably reappear later perhaps in another form.

*Dr Finkel now publishes *Health and Healing* magazine

AN INCREDIBLE SHOCK

THE sudden and untimely death of my wife, Bonnie, on 27th June, 1987, at the age of 73, was an incredible shock to me. It happened in a matter of seconds — she was alive and well one minute and dead the next. It was early morning when I noticed some sheep had got into the backyard, and we went outside to check on them. We both came back in to have breakfast together. Bonnie came into the kitchen about a minute before me and there I found her lying on the floor in front of the electric stove. As far as I could see, she had tripped on the mat, fallen backward and hit her head hard on the back of her chair. Her neck was broken. On the death certificate the doctor said she had died by a fall probably triggered by a heart attack. It was the same doctor who had been treating her for the heart trouble.

———————————

Section 2

This part of the book deals with the importance of minerals in the diet and what other people can tell us about cancer. But before hearing from the experts, we should perhaps check on the health of the natural realm, and in particular the state of our wildlife . . .

ENCOUNTERS WITH ANIMALS

MANY of the native animals that I was familiar with in my boyhood and teens are rarely seen today. What most people fail to realise is that when even the smallest of them are gone the health of the environment can suffer. Active little marsupials like the *Long-nosed Bandicoot* used to keep our bushland healthy by eating out the bardi grubs and witchetty grubs. They were superbly adapted to the task. Now there are grubby trees everywhere, and up in the hills barely a tree is free of white ants.

Some bandicoots are still about, but the job nature gave them is being neglected. In the days when they flourished, before they had predators such as feral cats and foxes stalking them, bandicoots lived in the hollows of trees. Now they live deep in vacated rabbit burrows mainly. And there were a great many other animals about that I fondly remember.

We don't see the duck-billed *Platypus* so much now. There used to be quite a few living in the creek up home. In years gone by we actually caught a family of them. They virtually lived on an insect diet and we couldn't provide that for long; they especially liked dragonflies. We still see the spiny *Echidna* — there's one out in the orchard all the time, eating fruit and insects.

The most ferocious marsupial I ever met was a *Spotted-tailed Quoll,* a carnivorous animal equipped with a gaping jaw. If it gets a bite of you, it can hang on like glue. He dug his sabre-like teeth into me and and wouldn't let go. I knew then it was not a rabbit caught in the trap!

It has been a long time since I saw a *Brush-tailed Phascogale* up close, although I'm sure there's one up in the roof right now. He can be heard thumping about after dusk. He goes out into the orchard at night and has a good feed. And, of course, leaves his calling card.

The sharped-toothed Spotted-tailed Quoll

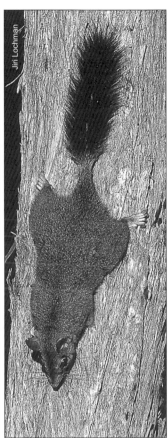

Indispensable: Long-nosed Bandicoot

Brush-tailed Phascogale

Echidna

Mountain Pygmy Possum

Jiri Lochman

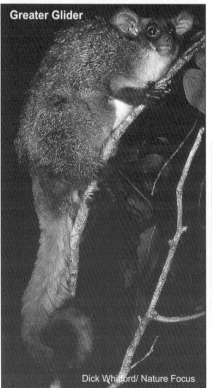

Greater Glider

Dick Whitford/ Nature Focus

Eastern Grey
Kangaroos

K. Atkinson

Bush Rat

Feathertail Glider   Parks Victoria

Another opportunist is *Triantelope*, the four-inch black spider who has recently kept me company in the kitchen. By day he sticks to the door of my refrigerator, motionless, and by night he turns hunter and keeps the house free of flies. He knows we won't hurt him.

The *Common Wombat* is still quite common in the northeast, and he is still blindly burrowing. These are powerful animals who like digging and can be great nuisances. They rip all the netting fences to pieces. In the early days 12 months after Brady fenced the property that I was eventually to own, the fence was riddled with holes scratched underneath. The place was swimming with rabbits when I took over and we tried ferrets to reduce the numbers. One day the ferrets got 17 rabbits after lunch, but they lacked stamina. The ferrets would get tired and go to sleep in the rabbit burrows! Myxomatosis, the viral disease spread by rabbit fleas that was systematically introduced by scientists, has reduced but not eradicated the rabbits, which are still about but do not thrive like they did in the early days.

I like to see the graceful *Eastern Grey Kangaroo* on the hill or hopping across the paddock. From the farmer's point of view, they're pretty harmless, unless you get a whole mob of them. The trouble is, they bring the dingoes in, which catch the young ones especially. Also running wild just over the river in the Buckland Valley, you may come upon descendants of the escaped horses of the pioneers, the wild brumbies, as they graze and gambol *in nooks that are grassy and wooded, where the soft spring rain sings a sweet refrain*, as Billy Wye aptly wrote.

In the hill country we used to catch glimpses of the *Large Forest Bat*, who lives on insects and moths, and we would be in awe watching the manoeuvres of the *Mopoke*, a native owl, as she fearlessly defended her territory against all comers, even hawks. We knew the habits of the gliding possums the little *Feathertail Glider*, which fed on insects, nectar and pollen of various trees and shrubs, and of the *Greater Glider*, who would only come down out of the trees as it was getting dark. One big fellow used to have a special place at the top of the main paddock. He would come zooming down to get a drink of water. Close to the end of the descent he'd aim for a convenient tree trunk and suddenly use his air brakes. This involved lifting up his head and the underside of his outstretched pelt to slow him down, and so he would land gracefully on the tree trunk on all fours. Once alighted and in the open he made sure of a tree close handy to shoot up if need be.

When we were young we could catch all sorts of things in the Porepunkah Gully, but the only pets I had were tame magpies. I remember the *Mountain Pygmy Possum* and the little *Bush Rat,* beautiful bush creatures. Foxes have just about cleaned those out now, absolutely murdered them. In fact, foxes have got rid of just about all the possums. After myxomatosis cut rabbit numbers they had to rely more on small native animals for a meal. But they were always omnivorous. When I was a boy, if we didn't close the fowl coup at night, we would lose everything to foxes. They were quite brazen. For example, one night two of them came and got a pair of chooks sitting on eggs just outside our back door. My father determined to outfox them. The next night he laid some bait and waited.

A fox took the bait and got the staggers. My father was ready for him. He sneaked up, caught him by the hind legs and swung him in a circle so he couldn't bite him. As I ran up to help carrying a broom handle, my father swung him low to keep him out of biting distance of me, grabbed the stick and whacked him on the head with it. We had no more problems from that fox. It was typical of George Weston that he knew how to handle the situation.

The fox has wrecked everything. It's the curse of the country, and the Lands Department has done very little to get rid of him. The trouble is the fox breeds so prolifically and is so adaptable across many terrains. Apart from a few sanctuaries, there isn't a place in Australia now where the wildlife is safe. Foxes were introduced, after rabbits, in the mid-19th century by enthusiasts of the Hunt. I can't say I had any fun hunting them. I used to catch 50 a year at least in my early days with the sheep. That was when I first used the hurricane lamp in the middle of the paddock that was later to prove so effective a deterrent against the dingo menace. Today there is a permanent dingo trapper located at Myrtleford and another a few kilometres away at Bright, and they go after foxes and other vermin. Dingoes, incidentally, are also partial to fruit. They love plums.

The domestic cat, of course, has been with us since the start, at least since 1882. They kill everything. I won't have a cat around the place. While you have a cat you have no birds.

IMPORTANT I.A.C.V.F. MEETINGS

THIS section deals with the most memorable of the meetings of the International Association of Cancer Victors and Friends that I attended. Although I was invited to be the association's guest speaker on two occasions and to field questions afterwards, no great advance in the fight against cancer was achieved. Even though the contents of my formula were freely disclosed, it is not an easy mixture to prepare and take. (For example, ferrous sulphate, being anhydrous, absorbs water of crystallisation between uses if the powder is not kept airtight, causing the mixture to clump). I suspect the main initial difficulty for most people was in obtaining supplies of the components, since most chemists were likely to stock only two or three of the eight salts.

Also, very accurate scales are needed to measure out correct weights, as well as a suitable grinder to powder the crystals and produce an even blend. Few people knew enough chemistry to trust themselves to get it right, and in any case the costs of making up small lots for private use were probably excessive. For these reasons I did not hear of anyone making up the powder themselves. For my own part, it was not till my patent was granted on the powder's use as a food supplement that I began to make it up in bulk. My procrastination was probably driven by an element of doubt as to its public acceptability after all those years of failing to interest the medical profession and health authorities.

One experiment in this period bolstered my confidence. As related earlier, since finding skin cancer in my sheep and curing them with the mineral lick, I wanted to know if melanomas in humans had the same cause, namely a diet rich in phosphorus. After Bonnie died I did not take my powder for four or five months, and did not worry too much about what I ate. So I would dine on eggs and meats and other danger foods regularly. Working in the hot sun, I soon developed four or five spots of melanoma in various places on exposed skin, including one on the point of the nose. I could feel a lump developing there. When I was satisfied it was going to cause trouble, I didn't let it go too far. I jumped on it straight away by dosing up again on the powder and going back to the right diet. In three or four months it was gone. After this I felt incredibly confident.

Here then are summaries of some of the most dynamic sessions sponsored by the IACVF with their fascinating insights into cancer, which gave support to my long-held theory about its origins and cure.

THE IAN GAWLER CASE

THERE was a big attendance on the night Dr Ian Gawler gave his talk on the ways he had achieved his recovery. People faced with cancer problems were anxious to know how a cure came about after he contracted cancer in the leg bone between knee and thigh. His cancer had not stopped with amputation of the leg, but spread over his chest and body, as he showed us in photographs. Despairing of obtaining a cure here, he flew to Europe and ended up in the clinic of a Dr Josef Issells, in Germany, where for more than three months he received treatment until it was deemed that the cancer was in remission, that is, that all the body cancer had cleared up. He then went to the Philippines where he sought the expertise of a naturopath to make certain of the cure. A diet of tropical fruits such as pineapple and paw paw, which are very low in phosphorus, and calf's liver, supplying niacin and cobalt, consolidated the remission. Questions were in order at the end of his talk so I rose to ask details of the treatment he had received from Dr Issells.

In reply he told the audience he had received a daily injection for 80 days of a vaccine known as BCG. This was made up by two French doctors, Calnette and Guerin, from weakened tuberculosis bacteria. My interpretation is that this germ gobbled up all the spare phosphorus in the bloodstream and starved the cancer out of existence. It is the same technique that an American doctor, William Cooley, employed around 1890 to cure cancer, though a different germ was used. In more recent times some doctors have used the Mixed Bacterium Vaccine (MBV) with similar results.

THE TONGA GROUP

AT one exciting session we heard from six people who claimed they had obtained remissions at the clinic of Dr Milan Brych*, in Tonga. They each lined up on the platform and told in turn of the type and location of the growth from which they suffered and how Dr Brych had treated them during their three-month stay in Tonga. These testimonies left no doubt in the large audience that the remissions were genuine and complete, so at the end I sought out two people to learn details.

On arrival at the clinic, they said, a sample of blood was taken from each of them and sent off for analysis. If any germs were found by the pathologist, these were cultured in a sterile medium and returned to Dr Brych in quantity. Each day patients received an injection of this personal vaccine until a remission was evident. Again tropical fruits were the major part of the diet. There was no advice about what to eat on their return home. Patients thought Dr Brych had no idea as to the *cause* of their cancer.

The improvement in their condition was short-lived, however. The IACVF, via its newsletters, kept us informed of the progress of several remission cases when they returned to Melbourne and resumed the diet of normal life (which caused the trouble in the first place). One after another it was reported that cancer had re-emerged and taken their lives.

COLDS AS SAFETY VALVE

THE use of such germ vaccines to obtain cancer remissions led me to investigate the role which the common cold may play in curbing abnormal and uncontrolled cell division, such as I saw induced many times by the application of phosphate fertiliser.

Phosphates are quickly absorbed into the bloodstream, so researchers have a hard time of it measuring and tracking them once in the body. Nor is phosphorus a constituent of protein — although no protein can be made without it. My medical texts told me that, in the form of adenosine di-phosphate (ATP) and adenosine tri-phosphate (ADP), phosphorus has the power to penetrate any cell in the body and commandeer nutrient elements from the intracellular fluid to make DNA, the code material for building new cells — either the body's own cells or those of invaders such as bacteria.

Excess phosphorus is eliminated from the body in the form of

---

*Dr Milan Brych was a controversial figure. Sections of the mass media in Australia branded him a charlatan. I am merely relating the testimonies of some of his patients.

soluble salts. Ions of phosphorus (a non-metal) combine readily with alkali (metallic) ions in solution and pass out in the urine. At least they do when there are enough alkali ions (the minerals potassium, magnesium, etc) available to combine with! If there is a disproportionate number of phosphate or phosphite ions present, phosphorus is not eliminated and creates havoc.

All it takes for phosphorus to build up in the body is a shortage of minerals present in the blood that are capable of neutralising it, particularly calcium. Without these to keep it in check, the highly active element phosphorus then goes to work on other elements to produce inflammation around the joints (arthritis). It goes into the growth of plaque cells that clog the arteries (vascular and heart disease). And it goes into the promotion of uncontrolled cell growth in any part of the body (cancer) according to the concentration and type of mineral it meets.

Now, as indicated in the remissions achieved with injected bacterial culture, the body has another, organic way to avert these life-threatening conditions. Conditions of over-supply of phosphorus in the blood encourage the rapid reproduction of germs (bacteria and viruses). The germs take up the phosphorus at the expense of the body's cells, and unhealthy tissue growth is checked.

I believe that the common cold is nature's safety valve against cancer. The temporary discomfort of having a cold is accompanied by a phosphorus-mopping-up operation as the germs take hold and multiply and eventually are taken out by the body's defence cells. After this battle, as the cold runs its course, the dead invaders and defenders are eliminated in copious amounts of mucus and phlegm, and the body returns to normal.

Keeping warm in bed and taking warm drinks of lemon juice and herbal honey to help the body eliminate harmful phosphorus is how I would treat a cold. If one kills a cold with a copious supply of alcohol or aspirin or some other concoction, one retains the phosphorus in the body to sponsor some other form of disease.

I am not advocating inaction against virulent and debilitating germs, of course. If the body's immune system requires help against these invaders it must be given.

Colds are the last resort of a body starved of correct mineral nutrition or loaded with phosphorus — same thing. It follows that colds are unnecessary. A correct diet will virtually eliminate them. Better to avoid the mildest cold altogether.

I notice that the Common Cold Centre in Britain has finally given up hope of finding a cure for colds after 10 years of painstaking research. According to its director, Professor Ron Eccles, the Cardiff University team will now devote its energies to finding means of preventing colds and minimising the symptoms. "The [cold] virus is impossible to cure," he is quoted as saying in *The Age* (12/11/98). "The trouble is that there are at least 200 viruses that cause the common cold. It is not just one disease. Even if a cure for one were found, it would soon be redundant. People would then be susceptible to hundreds of other viruses waiting to invade. I don't think the public appreciates the magnitude of the problem we have been faced with this past decade." Perhaps someone will take pity on their plight. Send them a copy of this book.

ALL THOSE POSSIBLE CURES

OVER the years the IACVF has arranged to present any speaker with a novel approach to cancer or with facts about a promising compound or new drug. They included Dr Ainslie Meares, whose advocacy of meditation won some converts. Then there were the Indian yogis, with their peculiar methods of fasting and meditation. Fasting should always be of some help to a cancer sufferer in that, if you curtail the intake of phosphorus, you restrict the growth of cancer.

Dr Alex Forbes, who directed a large cancer clinic in Bristol, UK, gave an enthralling talk on the methods used to treat patients there — apparently just about every technique known to the medical world. In a brief interview, I told him of the cures I had achieved, but did not have time before he was invited to speak to give details about the powder. He took my address, but no inquiry eventuated. He was a busy man.

Advocates of vitamin treatments at the time gave much factual evidence for their support and use. Discussions showed that, while vitamins gave some benefit, full remissions did not come. Phosphorus will combine readily with every other nutrient element and especially vitamin C ($C_6H_8O_6$) and vitamin E ($C_{29}H_{50}O$). These are soon broken down in the body, however, which suggests that to have lasting effect they would need to be supplied continuously and in greater dosage than would be normal and convenient in the diet. But, as I mentioned earlier — see *Experiments with Vitamins* — there have been improvements. Recently I read Dr Ruth Cilento's famous book* on vitamin C, which has plenty of preventative advice, but no mention in the index of the chief cancer culprit, phosphorus.

Many types of foods or diets became subjects of discussion. Among these was apricot kernels and garlic, which had some tonic effect but little cure. Both have a dangerous content of phosphorus like most seeds, but this is mitigated to some extent by a high content of magnesium, which tends to keep intestines healthy. For many years apricot kernels were used to extract the amygdalin, also known as laetrile or vitamin B17. Another source is bitter almonds. Its use as a cancer therapy was promoted by the late Dr. Ernst T. Krebs, of San Francisco. US National Cancer Institute tests in 1981 claimed it to be a dangerous therapy due to a build-up of high levels of cyanide and also ineffective, which of course was denied by patients who benefited from it.

The diet that has maintained a good reputation over many years is that advocated by Dr Max Gerson of Germany. Some 75 to 80 per cent of the foods in it have a low phosphorus content. Unfortunately, some foods included have a high content, which if taken in excess would prove dangerous. The Gerson diet is not foolproof and will only become safe when *all* the foods in it are low in phosphorus. This would be possible tomorrow if more chemical analyses of foods were available. I estimate from the books and charts I have studied that only about half the job has been done. The best effort to date, I believe, is *Cancer-Fighting Foods* by Health Research, published by Book Bin, in which I have been at pains to rate as wide a range of foods as possible which are common in the Australian and British diets.

One of the most intriguing stories of battling cancer is that given by Johanna Brandt, a nurse from South Africa, in her booklet, *The Grape Cure.* She got so close to the control of her breast cancer that I am sure she would have solved the enigma of cancer had she a better knowledge of chemistry and the analyses of foods. What she did not know was the

*Heal Cancer — Choose Your Own Survival Path (1994)

difference in content of phosphorus between black and white grapes. While white grapes are safe enough to give a cure, black grapes are dangerous in the diet of a cancer patient in that they contain almost double the amount of phosphorus and help a growth. Though her booklet gave the full story, I believe that had she consumed only white grapes along with the fasting and use of ice packs on the growth, she could have had a complete cure.

THE LINXIAN STORY

THE most extraordinary story in the cancer saga which gives ample indication of its cause comes out of China. The north-central region of Linxian, in Henan province, has recently gone from having one of the lowest incidences of cancer in the world to one of the highest in only 15 years. I first learned of this alarming epidemic through a three-part program on ABC-TV.

The introduction to the program told us that the district of Linxian carried a dense population whose standard of living had become a matter of worry for the authorities. For more than 4,000 years the Chinese nation had a record of healthy living, their diet consisting mainly of white rice, fruits, vegetables and a little meat. The local health authorities looked at other countries and decided they could improve their own health standards by encouraging people to adopt a more varied diet. Small trials showed that, just as they had been handling rice for centuries, it would be possible to harvest both wheat and maize in similar fashion without expensive machinery.

So supplies of seed were bought from other countries and distributed among the peasant farmers. In two or three years they were producing good crops of both wheat and maize, and the methods used by Mr Kellogg were used to make bread and breakfast cereals for the population. As grain supplies increased it became possible to greatly increase pig and poultry numbers, making plenty of meat and eggs available for the people.

Anyone who has read the book *Farmers of Forty Centuries,* by F.H. King, should be well aware of the ways by which Chinese farmers maintained the fertility of their soils over 4,000 years . . .by always following the law of return, using the wastes of vegetable matter along with all animal and human excreta as compost, to grow foods organically. They have a record of health and longevity that far surpasses that of any other nation. The soils of Linxian province are quite rich in phosphorus, so after living on the grains and foods which they produced for four or five years, the results began to emerge. Cancer lesions would form on pigs' ears, on the combs and lobes of hens, and anywhere on humans. It was not long before the figures for human cancers soared to the world's highest.

It did not take me long to realise that the grain diet that had caused such a calamity in Linxian was almost identical to that which had me in trouble in 1933 and 1943. The very important lesson to be learned from such events is that it takes only four or five years on a diet even moderately rich in phosphorus before the immune system is weakened and both animals and humans end up diseased.

It seems to me that the medical world does not realise how phosphorus can create a whole range of viral diseases that can dominate human life from the moment of conception to death. When you get excess phosphorus in your body it will either breed germs, produce cell multiplication, or paralyse.

MYSTERY OF THE VIRUSES

RECENTLY when giving a talk to a medical interest group, I asked if they could tell me the definition of a virus. One person spoke up. He said facetiously that it was a disease you caught when the doctor did not know what it was. The reply perhaps reflects on the current state of knowledge about viruses, which in recent years have greatly increased in their trouble-making activity. What activates these inert, harmless bits of nucleic acid in a protein overcoat and causes them to change into virulent pathogens is the same mechanism that enables bacteria to multiply exponentially, as described above ('Cold as Safety Valve').

From the time of Louis Pasteur up until World War 2, bacteria of all sorts caused most diseases. Since the war, hormones, radioactivity, and viruses have arrived to complicate the prognosis. The electron microscope has enabled researchers to isolate and identify most of the new viruses, but new ones keep coming.

IS NO FOOD SAFE?

IT is easy enough to land oneself in trouble by living on a group of foods naturally rich in phosphorus. But nowadays that hazard is increased by the fact that most commercially grown foods have phosphorus added via sprays and fertilisers.

It was no surprise to me to learn, when examining Victoria's figures for the incidence of cancer in cattle in recent years that slowly but surely the number of cases for which compensation has been paid is accelerating (see Appendix C). The state figures for sheep mortality might also be interesting, if records were kept. They are not, on the rationalisation that a sheep is more likely to finish its days at the slaughterhouse before ever a cancer runs its course.

Nowadays you have got double and triple super being applied — twice and three times the amount of phosphorus as in the original product. The rationale firstly is that it's a little over half the volume, saving a lot of the freight cost, and secondly it goes a lot further: you don't have to apply so much, probably two-thirds, or three parts, with the seed.

What this means is that the plant has got more phosphorus available to it very rapidly without the other minerals to balance. In other words, the plant takes it up first, because it is most soluble, to the exclusion of the other minerals needed for balanced growth, which are in chronic short supply in the plant.

You may have heard of farms being quarantined after harmful residues have been found in the meat of the animals. Very often it's due to farmers' over-use of a systemic insecticide like dieldrin, an organochlorine chemical which becomes locked up in the fat component of the meat of the animal. Phosphorus in tissue is much harder to measure, but herbivorous animals are at the same time absorbing phosphorus as well.

Over the years I have seen a lot of idiocies perpetrated on farmers in the name of science and progress. You have only to look at our polluted rivers and barren or salty soils to see where it has got us. East Gippsland's lakes are being choked by chemicals and silt from agricultural runoff. The soils of northern Victoria and the Riverina are half dead. Sheep farmers there are having many of the same problems that I experienced 40 years ago. When I began to use the licks, the switch-over was dramatic. It supplied the nutrients to the animals. It wasn't very expensive, and far less work. The sheep took it up in the lick and distributed it all over the farm in their droppings and urine.

I believe we can live in harmony with nature as the Creator intended if we get back to first principles of sensible diet and responsible farming practices.

DR JOEL WALLACH

THE modern diet lacks mineral nutrition simply because our soils lack minerals. Trace elements such as iron, manganese, copper, zinc, cobalt, selenium, chromium and boron that once would have returned to the soil naturally in plant and animal wastes on many a farm are now depleted or missing. And returning them to the soil artificially is too expensive a business for many of today's farmers. The use of fertilisers can further distort the mineral balance of the main elements in food, as I found in my experiments with super. Yet the link between minerally unbalanced foods and the rise of chronic and degenerative diseases in the 20th century is plain to see for those who will look.

Convincing people of this, and especially the medical profession, is not easy, as the career of Dr Joel Wallach illustrates. A farm boy from Missouri, he became a vet and began a life-long crusade to get people interested in nutrition. I listened recently to a widely circulated tape recording of a talk he gave in 1994 entitled "Dead Doctors Don't Lie".

On his family's farm which grew corn and soyabeans for a cattle feed-lot operation, they knew how to "do feed and nutrition" for cows and still make money, he said. To the choice feed they added all sorts of health-giving vitamin and mineral supplements for the calves. To their own food they added nothing. If they got sick, it was too bad; the cost would just be booked up to the numbingly more expensive human-type medical system.

Wallach studied agriculture at university and then went on to veterinary school. He then visited Africa to work with elephants and rhinos, and two years later accepted a job at St Louis Zoo conducting autopsies of animals who died of natural causes. Over 12 years he claims to have done 17,500 autopsies on 454 species of animals from many zoos and on 3,000 human beings who had lived close to zoos.

His fascinating finding was that "every animal and human being who dies of natural causes dies of a nutritional deficiency". He wrote scientific papers about his work, contributed articles to textbooks, wrote for newspapers and magazines, and went on TV but "couldn't get anybody excited about nutrition back in the '60s." So he went back to school and became a physician. "And they allowed me to use everything I'd learned in veterinary school about nutrition on my human patients," he said. "And, no surprise to me, it worked". He spent 12 years in general practice in Oregon. As the message has not got through yet, he continues his crusade.

The "dead doctors" of the title of his talk refers to his statistic that the average life span of doctors in his country is 58 years compared with the average for their patients of 75.5 years. (For Australians, according to the Anti-Cancer Council of Victoria, average life expectancy is 82 years for women and 76 for men.) Wallach is particularly hard on the US medical profession for giving wrong advice and not adopting and publicising, for many conditions, the cures he said were found by veterinarians 50 years or more years ago. These include ulcers, which are not caused by tension but by the germ helicobacter pylori (and cured with bismuth and tetracycline); cardiomyopathy (cured with selenium), Alzheimer's disease (cured in its early stages with high doses of vitamin E and low doses of vegetable oil), osteoporosis including kidney stones and low back pain (cured with calcium supplement, and boron), aneurisms (cured with a copper supplement), some types of arthritis (with gelatin), and diabetes (with the trace minerals chromium and vanadium).

Other conditions curable with minerals, he claims, quoting scientific support, are premenstrual tension or PMT ("to relieve 85 per cent of the emotional and physical symptoms, take twice the recommended daily dose of calcium"); grey hair, facial and body-skin wrinkles, varicose veins, sagging under the arms, legs, belly or breast (take some copper supplement); liver spots or age spots on the face or hands or "radical damage" (take selenium supplement); male-pattern baldness (take a tin supplement); low blood sugar (take chromium and vanadium and so avoid diabetes); losing your senses of taste and smell (take a zinc supplement); learning disabilities, bone problems, anaemia, a craving for sweets or dirt (give a general mineral supplement).

Wallach has identified 157 different diseases caused by calcium deficiency. Among them is osteoporosis of the joint ends of bones implicated, he says, in 85 per cent of all cases of arthritis, including lumbago and sciatica. He regards grey hair as the first sign of copper deficiency, regardless of age, and a dose of copper can restore natural color. As copper controls the health of the body's elastic fibres, he says, returning it to the diet can banish crows-feet, body wrinkles and sagging. His advice to would-be dieters is to take no notice of best-selling medical authors who write about nutrition and die practising what they preach at the age of 40. Rather, people should ensure they get all the 90 nutrients they need in their daily diet "in complete numbers and optimal amounts" . . . including some 60 minerals and 16 vitamins.

WHY SUPPLEMENTS?

PRACTICALLY speaking, as farm soils tend to be depleted of minerals or contain dangerous amounts of phosphorus, as we have seen, this means supplementing food with minerals and vitamins. The extra minerals should be taken in colloidal form. The cost of about a dollar a day compares with paying "a gob of money" if you get a nutritional-deficiency disease. Although this advice is admirable, Wallach seems unaware of the need to first choose a diet based on foods correctly balanced for phosphorus. Also, standard artificial vitamin supplements come mixed up with phosphates to make them soluble, and this type should be avoided. I would expect the fruit of any fruit tree that has a deep tap root to be naturally loaded with trace minerals. And one should be careful of over-dosing. To take just one example from the land, at Norong weeds rich in copper could kill off sheep like nine pins.

Wallach's discussion of colloidal minerals is interesting. These are minerals that have been absorbed by plants; they are 7000 times smaller than a red blood cell and negatively charged, making them 98 per cent absorbable and easily attracted to the (positively charged) lining of the gut. The source of the product he endorses is a prehistoric rain-forest deposit in southern Utah in which the mineral-rich vegetation has been uniquely preserved like hay. A sample is prepared by being ground into a flour, and soaked for three or four weeks in filtered spring water until it reaches a concentration of 38 grams per litre for bottling. By analysis it has more than 60 colloidal minerals and trace minerals in it. Colloidal minerals are absorbed more readily into the bloodstream than manufactured chelated minerals, which comprise a metal coated by an amino acid or enzyme.

Given full nutrition with colloidal minerals and a sensible lifestyle, Wallach reckons we should all live active lives to our genetic potential of 120 to 140 years. Only five cultures do this already — in Tibet, East Pakistan, Georgia, Ecuador and SE Peru — and they have a couple of things in common. All live in mountain villages which receive less than 5mm of rain a year, and all get their drinking water and irrigation water for their crops from the meltwater of glaciers. This glacial "milk", the product of ground-up rocks, "contains 60 to 72 minerals". I should think that in such crops a surplus of phosphorus would be most unlikely.

According to the World Health Organisation, men and women in Australia on average lead a *healthy* life for 73.2 years. And what follows then? By implication, sickness. In the above cultures where old age is not associated with ill health, this would be considered shocking. And so would a health system like Australia's costing an annual $US1600 per person to run.

Wallach's incisive talk left me with an enduring image, when he recalled an article in the January 1973 edition of *National Geographic* dealing with people who habitually live to age 120 and beyond. As he tells it, the magazine featured a picture of "a lady who is 136 years old. She was sitting in a wicker chair with a big Cuban cigar in one hand and an eight-ounce glass of vodka in the other, and she was partying. She was not in a nursing home, slouched over and ready to have someone take another $125 out of her chequeing account." Hear, hear! If I may offer myself as an example, old age need not make senile old cripples out of us.

ANTIOXIDANTS

SCIENTISTS tell us that cancer results from cell mutation when cells sustain damage to their DNA, the genetic code that tells them how to duplicate. And so cancerous cells are abnormal cells. The mutations are caused when free radicals get into a cell and damage the DNA structure.

We are discussing here something that cannot be seen but is happening at the level of atoms and molecules.

Free radicals are unstable oxidant atoms which will "borrow" electrons from any available healthy cells such as fatty acids, turning them rancid. The body is producing free radicals constantly, both during metabolism and strenuous exercise, and in the normal scavenging of the white blood cells to eliminate foreign invaders. To prevent the havoc which these resulting free radicals could unleash, the body makes its own antioxidants to neutralise them.*

Today most food production relies on heavy applications of artificial fertilisers, contributing to the mineral imbalance. Thousands of chemicals and solvents have come into our environment as contaminants and pollutants, including the phosphates. Above us, the hole in the ozone layer grows ever bigger, exposing us and our crops to abnormal doses of ultraviolet radiation. (In recent years the heat of the sun has scorched my apple crop.)

At the same time cancer is on the rise in the community at large, and there is a proliferation of new diseases such as asthma, arthritis, chronic fatigue syndrome, coronary disease, multiple sclerosis, adult-onset diabetes and osteoporosis, none of which was common in my youth.

This has led some chemists to conclude that 20th century humans are losing the battle against free-radical production and in need of help. They have come up with a 21st century remedy: more powerful antioxidants — herbal, mineral and vitamin — to supplement the diet.

The main mineral antioxidants are zinc (available in colloidal form or chelated) and selenium, which must be in trace amounts.

The antioxidant vitamins are A (and its precursor, beta-carotene), C and E. All are essential to nutrition as well, but an overdose may be unwise. In the case of beta-carotene the optimum dose is 2-18mg a day, but a dosage greater than this proves to be worse than not taking the vitamin at all.*

Taking megadoses of vitamin C is found in many studies to prevent

---

* Thus superoxide dismutase acts on the common free radical, superoxide, to convert it to hydrogen peroxide. Two other antioxidants, glutathione peroxidase and catalase, then convert the hydrogen perioxide into water and oxygen.

cell mutations, but the body can retain little of the vitamin in this form, as it is excreted and passes out into the urine almost immediately. And high supplementation with vitamin E has been shown to suppress the immune system.**

What the chemists have come up with to get around these problems is a new family of natural chemicals known as the proanthocyanidins. These are said to be 30 to 50 times more powerful as antioxidants than even vitamins C and E and only microdoses are needed, which should cut costs and prevent wastage. Proanthocyanidins can be used as a food supplement in place of vitamins A and E or, better still, combined with them.

Combined with vitamin C in the presence of bioflavonoids (vitamin P) a synergy is produced which enables vitamin C to be retained by the body for up to 72 hours. A promising source of extracted pyroanthocyanidins is the seed of the dark grape *Vitis vinifera**** which is missing the trace pesticides and fungicides of longer-lived plants. Other sources include bilberry fruit and lime flour.

FOODS CAUSING CANCER

IN most developed countries the situation in the home and the supermarket is identical with that obtaining in research institutions. People have little idea of what foods cause cancer. But farming trends in recent years have produced a dangerous situation. Chemical reactions in soils can be very variable and complex. Fresh cows' milk can be especially dangerous in late autumn or early winter if irrigation water or rain has dissolved phosphorus from an application of super, and so loaded up fast-growing pastures. Cows milked twice daily can pass on such an excess.

Most meats, especially grain-fed types such as pork and poultry, are

*Hathcock, J.N., Hatlan, D.G., Jenkins, M.Y., McDonald, J.T., Sundaresan, P.R., Wilkening, V.N., "Evaluation of Vitamin A Toxicity," American Journal of Clinical Nutrition., 52 (2) 183-202 (1990).

** Huttunen, J., (in) Spring Report of the Finnish National Public Health Institution (1994).

***This is good news for wine drinkers. Red wine in moderation may protect against cancer because of the ready supply of antioxidant absorbed from the seed during fermentation.

rich in phosphorus. All grains and dairy products, many vegetables and a few fruits are rich in phosphorus. In addition, the processed foods we buy contain phosphorus-based seasonings and preservatives. Even in self-raising flour, phosphorus compounds have replaced the customary baking soda. In confectionery and soft drinks, a natural sweetener such as cane sugar has largely been eclipsed by phosphorus-rich corn syrup. Phosphorus-rich foods become a health hazard when consumed collectively.

So how safe are commercially grown fruit and vegetables among the foods to make up any anti-cancer diet? Clearly the best to buy is organically grown or what you can grow yourself. And if you grow them yourself, you should stick with safe sprays and insecticides.

In my own orchard for 10 years I have successfully used a night trap for the codling moth, which likes to lay its eggs in apples and pears. It consists of a 75W pearl electric lightbulb suspended 5cm above a dish of water containing a spoonful of kerosene. The moth is attracted by the light, hits the bulb and falls down into the water. No moth that lands in that water escapes. They can stay alive in the water for 10 or 12 hours. The kerosene is optional, but kills the moths instantly. I have found this one trap to be very efficient at keeping the fruit trees in my orchard free of insect infestation. Other bugs trapped include aphids, thrip, Rutherglen, leafhoppers, mites and spiders — if they fly or move they get caught. Kerosene applied in a thin film also prevents mosquitoes breeding up in the water supply. A capful does an entire dam.

TOBACCO HOME TRUTHS

AS I see it now, the great danger with the modern cigarette is the mixture of deadly gases liberated during combustion. As cigarette tobacco is now grown, it is possible to get a mixture of these gases as the chemical components produce:

MORE carbon monoxide as the excess phosphorus makes the leaf burn hotter.

PHOSPHORUS trioxide or pentoxide from fertiliser and organic spray — it is the main agent causing paralysis (asthma and emphysema) and cancer.

PHOSGENE, a gas from the mixture of carbon monoxide and chlorine in BHC or dieldrin.

PHOSPINE gas, as moisture from the smoker's mucous membranes give up hydrogen to form PH3.

Also associated are:

CADMIUM in trace amounts from superphosphate — it accumulates in arteries and kidneys and leads over time to high blood pressure, atherosclerosis and renal failure. (Traces also in foods grown with super with same result.)

CARBON disulphide, from carbon monoxide and sulphur in super and sulphate fertilisers.

NITROSAMINES, which are potent carcinogens.

TAR gases from the phenyl, ethane and miscible oils in other sprays.

According to a report in the *British Medical Journal* (December 1996), cigarette smoke contains a cocktail of 4000 chemicals, including 43 known carcinogens. Tobacco grown more naturally does not carry such a lethal concoction.

There is good scientific evidence that the havoc wreaked inside the body by smoking is reflected in the smoker's physical appearance — in premature wrinkles on the face, grey hair, and baldness. Evidence has even come to light that smoking destroys nerve endings at the back of the eyes, directly causing vision impairment and blindness. The link between smoking and lung cancer is well known, and even admitted by cigarette companies.

Yet I do not support calls to "discourage production, promotion and use of tobacco in any form", as recommended in one study.* Between 1918 and 1928 in my youth, before Virginia leaf was grown in Victoria, people were never in trouble smoking natural tobacco. (For recent figures on lung cancer, and from 40 years ago, see Appendix D.)

What needs to change is the way cigarettes are made. Surely there ought to be closer liaison between farmers and agricultural chemists to produce safer tobacco and eliminate additives.

---

* The 670-page report, *Food, Nutrition and the Prevention of Cancer: a global perspective*, sponsored by the American Institute for Cancer Research, 1997.

SPECIFIC CASES

THE vulnerability of smokers or inhalers of cigarette-tobacco smoke already predisposed to cancer by a phosphorus-rich diet is, of course, heightened by the action of phosphoric gases on throat and lungs. People in the same dietary category also are in danger of contracting bowel cancer through a shortage of calcium in the tissues.

In the same way a shortage of iodine and excess phosphorus can lead to growths in the throat and thyroid glands. Natural foods contain comparatively little free sodium, an element essential in the excretion of surplus phosphorus and chlorine.   In its free form, which may be introduced into the body as bicarbonate of soda, sodium takes out chlorine and phosphorus. In the form of common salt, used in many processed foods and beverages, sodium is not so available for such reactions, and a build-up of common salt and phosphorus in the body may lead to kidney breakdown.

I am struck now with the plight of thousands of people of assorted ages who are confined in institutions with the nerve-wasting disease, multiple sclerosis. I have read of MS victims being given temporary relief from their paralysis by a drug familiarly known as L-Dopa. But they had no dietary relief, of course, and relapsed. A natural diet rich in calcium, iron, potassium and magnesium can work wonders.

CURBING CANCER CULPRITS

WE have many visitors to the farm. They include people on holiday in the valley who call in to buy our walnuts and chestnuts. A couple of years ago we were asked about "green" fruit from our black walnut trees (*Juglans nigra*). The trees are named for their dark brown hardwood — when not being grown for walnuts the wood is ideal for making furniture and gunstocks due to its strength, durability and lightness.

This inquiry must have come between mid-December and early February, as we had some nuts to sell. (The nuts are normally picked from early February after they have ripened and darkened.) Then other people began to ask after the unripened nuts. One said the hulls contained a miraculous pesticide which could cure cancer. So my interest was aroused. More recently I learned the full story.

A North American biologist and naturopath, Hulda Regehr Clark, has published some interesting findings on the relationship between parasites and cancer, and her casebook makes riveting reading. Black-walnut hulls are used in treating her patients, since the hulls when still green are said to contain a substance that kills internal parasites. It is parasites she blames for promoting tumors — for details, see Appendix B — in league with bacteria, fungi, inorganic copper, cobalt and vanadium, malonic acid, and assorted carcinogens.

This grand conspiracy theory of tumor production is supported by an impressive body of evidence — more than 100 documented studies of her patients before and after treatment to remove these so-called cancer-promoting agents. Their cancers and other signs of poor health are reported to have cleared up once they took the self-administered treatment seriously and followed it rigorously. The goals of her treatment are to kill parasites, encysted eggs and microbes; to eliminate sources of isopropyl alcohol; and to warn people off commercial body products and foods micro-contaminated with industrial solvents and metals.

There are parallels here with the treatments I devised decades ago to cure my leukemia (1934) and the cancerous welt on my hand (1942). As related, when our soils went on strike in 1933-34 after the successive heavy applications of phosphate to tobacco crops, my own health took a dive. The weeds went on a growth spurt and there was a marked increase in activity by beetles, leaf hoppers, grubs and every kind of sucking insect. I don't know with certainty if parasites and bacteria conspired to make me sick with leukemia then, or were responsible for the tumor — I had no way to test this — but I think it is very probable, as everything around me was going wild under the influence of phosphorus.

I was able to beat cancer by means of a better balanced diet of fresh unprocessed foods supplemented with a level teaspoon of my alkaline-formula powder in the juice of half a lemon. (Today the formula is stronger, with the dosage to treat a person of 65kg and under being a mere ˘ teaspoon a day for seven days and then ° teaspoon every second day.) The salts in the supplement were chosen for their solubility but the sulphate salts I used are renown also for their germicidal action. One of them, magnesium sulphate, or Epson salts, also kills tapeworms. Sulphur in salt licks given to my sheep and my policy of curbing our use of phosphate on pasture throughout the 1950s certainly inhibited the usual farm diseases such as foot-abscess, foot rot, pink-eye, pisal rot and clostridiums. And our sheep had very few problems with worms.

As to heavy metals causing disease, this is not surprising. Cadmium is a good example. It is commonly listed as a trace contaminant on bags of artificial fertiliser. It is in our foods because they are grown in superphosphate. Cadmium is so much a part of agriculture today that obtaining food with no trace of it may be close to impossible. Cadmium's action is to promote the build-up of cholesterol plaques in arteries* in conjunction with phosphorus. If it were not in our food due to super, heart disease, the No. 2 killer of Australians, would scarcely be a problem.**

A SPOONFUL OF SULPHUR

IN an earlier chapter I told how my mother kept her children healthy with drinks of lemon and Epsom salts, and weekly line-ups to administer treacle and sulphur. Hulda Clark apparently had similar treatment from her mother 60 or more years ago: regular force-feeding with a spoonful of sulphur and molasses and raw onion. She laments now that such wise practices, which kept germs and parasites at bay, have been forsaken. What still concerns her, and me, are the real problems that cancer blinds our society to: the way modern farming and manufacturing practices have brought unwanted chemicals into the food chain leading to an overpowering of the body's defences against invaders.

The first step in science, if you want your theory to be taken seriously, is to collect the evidence for it. In this Dr Clark (she holds a PhD in physiology) has had the advantage over other cancer researchers. She collected and verified her evidence by designing an inexpensive and safe

---

* Raymont, W.D., Wells, J.R., Yamamoto, K., "Further Studies on the Relationship between Trace Cadmium Residues and Arterial Deposition of Cholesterol," PDF Report, WHO/CU (1979).

** In 1995 more than 2.8 million Australians had a cardiovascular condition, commonly marked by high blood pressure, the Australian Institute of Health and Welfare reported. Heart disease and stroke claimed a life every 12 minutes. The cost of treatment in 1994 figures was $3.7 billion a year.

new tool to look at what is going on deep inside the human body. It is a remarkable electronic gadget which permits disease "agents" to be identified in a simple and non-invasive way. She calls it a Syncrometer™. (For how it works, see Appendix B.)

By electronic means, she has identified the above-mentioned "conspirators" as being present in *all* cancers. Knowing *what* they are and *where* they are in the body has enabled her to devise simple strategies to remove them one by one in order to give the body a chance to mend the damage. She reports that once the invaders are gone, tumors rapidly shrink, or at least cease to grow, and that many other indicators of poor health disappear. Taking this a step further and tackling surplus phosphorus in the diet, I am sure, would make for lasting recoveries.

He own success at clearing up tumors has led her to conclude, as I did many years ago, that cancer is *not* the pernicious, fatal disease we all thought but one that can soon be turned around. The downside of her approach is that patients whose diets are loaded with phosphorus or lacking in alkali minerals could soon go down with cancer again, despite Dr Clark's best efforts, as the microbes recolonise their bodies and initiate new tumors. And indeed reinfection is something she constantly warns about.

PURGING SLIMY INVADERS

THE link between an unbalanced diet and contracting a disease seems an elementary one to make. And I have no doubt, based on many years of experience in animal husbandry, that the continuation of a mineral imalance in blood wherein surplus phosphorus cannot be eliminated brings about the conditions necessary for tumors to develop. Less clear has been how. The explanations based on microbiology that Dr Clark offers seem quite plausible. Her independent research throws down the gauntlet to the medical profession.

The native American people, she says, knew that humans were parasitized, just like animals are, and had frequent purgings that included diarrhea or vomiting to rid themselves of "slimy invaders". Many other native peoples did the same, and traditional herbal remedies have been handed down which can safely be used to kill the many type of tapeworm.

Compare this with the deworming tablet you buy from the chemist, which may be effective against only one or two types of work. Some parasites are common in humans.

Their eggs may be alive in undercooked meat and dairy products, or attached to unwashed vegetables from manure when they enter our bodies and then develop there; many more come to us courtesy of pets and domestic animals. But the most common form is the microscopic larval stage — or rather stages, since each parasite can have several forms with no obvious resemblance to each other but each contributing a part of the organism's life cycle. These are generally dormant inside the human host.

The chief of the invaders Dr Clark is concerned about, *the* critical parasite in cancer, is the common, leaf-shaped intestinal adult fluke, *Fasciolopsis buskii* (about 3cm long). Normally this member of the flatworm family lies quietly attached to the intestine absorbing nutrients from our food as it fills up with eggs. Strings of millions of eggs from it will pass out with the bowel motion, although some hatch in the bowel. A few eggs may pass through tiny lesions which can develop from time to time in the lining of the bowel. They may be pulled into the bloodstream and from there be attracted to weak or damaged organs. The eggs and redia stages may lodge in areas where there is scarring, benign lumps, poor circulation, glands containing a build-up of heavy metals. While it is living in the gut, the worm won't give its host much trouble, says Dr Clark. But this is a generalisation; for some people the worm's activity in the bowel may result in Crohn's disease, frequent bouts of colitis, or irritable bowel syndrome, she says.

Fasciolopsis is of special interest to her for two reasons: When its eggs hatch, she has discovered with the Syncrometer, they release a powerful growth factor that acts on the surrounding cells so that benign tumors quickly turn malignant. And being able to leave the intestine and develop in other parts of the body means the worm can multiply itself at every stage of its life cycle at a frantic pace.

It used to be thought this was impossible. Any farmer or biology student knows that the hatchlings of intestinal flukes need an outside host, such as a snail in a pond, in which to develop and so continue the fluke's multifarious life cycle. On the farm we were familiar with parasites such as the hydatid *Echinococcus granulosus*, which lives in the intestine of dogs and produces hundreds of sticky eggs at a time. These pass out with the dog's faeces and may stick to the dog's hair or to grass. A sheep or cow can then become host to the tapeworm by eating the grass. The tapeworm embryo that develops from the egg may burrow through the wall of the sheep's intestine into the bloodstream, and lodge in its liver or lungs. It grows into a cyst . . . from which spring millions more progeny. If the farmer should kill the sheep for meat, and feed the offal or uncooked meat to the dogs, the hydatid stage can attach itself to the dog's intestine and grow into an adult tapeworm. Cycle complete.

EXTRAORDINARY

DR CLARK identifies the adult human intestinal fluke, Fasciolopsis, making itself at home in the livers of cancer patients. For it to successfully colonise the human liver without needing an outside host for any of four pre-adult larval stages something extraordinary must be happening. According to Dr Clark, this abnormal condition is the "tragic" pollution of the body with isopropyl alcohol (or *isopropanol*) which accumulates in the liver. The solvent must be able to dissolve the hard outer casing of the cocoon-like final metacercaria stage of the flatworm.

Whenever she detects the adult fluke in the liver, isopropanol is always present in the liver too. How does it get there? Colorless liquid isopropanol is cleaning alcohol. It is also used in the manufacture of antifreeze and as a solvent. Manufacturers use it to sterilise their food-handling equipment. Dr Clark's Syncometer finds isopropanol mainly in cosmetics, where it is commonly used as an antiseptic and in other body products including toothpaste, mouthwash, body lotion, shampoo, hair spray, mousse, shaving supplies and rubbing alcohols. Isopropanol is readily absorbed through the skin. In processed foods it may be present in smaller amounts (parts per million).

A secondary source of the chemical turns out to be clostridium bacteria that manufacture isopropanol in the digestive tract and "under dental restorations" where the dentist has not thoroughly disinfected a wound. Dr Clark reports finding all six species of clostridium bacteria in the intestinal tract of cancer patients. And only in cancer patients do clostridium species invade the upper parts, including stomach and oesophagus.

My sulphate salts cleared up clostridium in my sheep, and I believe the current mixture does the same job today in human patients.

LIVER COLONISED

WHY be so concerned about this isopropanol? Because Dr Clark has found that 100 per cent of cancer patients have isopropanol accumulated in the liver and in their cancerous tissues.

It does not follow that all people who use cosmetics containing isopropanol necessarily contract cancer, since in most cases their livers will detoxify isopropanol for them. And indeed people without cancer always test negative to having isopropanol in their livers; that is, they are free of it, and free of fluke in the liver.

So why can't the cancer group detoxify isopropanol? Dr Clark finds a mould byproduct known as aflatoxin B in their livers. Aflatoxins are produced by mouldy food. That they should end up in the liver, of all organs, is not surprising as the liver is the body's main cleanser and filter. But the coincidence is not a happy one, because this common fungal toxin poisons the liver's ability to detoxify isopropanol and can itself cause tumors in the liver.

The remedy against mycotoxins, I think, is clear. Apart from storing food safely and throwing out mouldy food, one should change to a low-phosphorus diet, since fungi do not flourish in a phosphorus-poor environment. (To see what I mean, try growing mushrooms without fertiliser!) Limiting phosphorus will curb the disruptive aflatoxin production of fungi and allow the liver to get on with the vital job of breaking down isopropanol and other toxins in its enzyme pathways.

A further point about these mycelia growths in the body is that Dr Clark sees them only in the presence of elemental (inorganic) copper. Most likely copper has leached out of household plumbing and copper hot-water systems into drinking water, or from metal tooth fillings. She notes that when copper pipes are replaced by PVC and dental fillings with non-toxic methyl methacrylate, copper levels fall in less than a week. Blood building resumes immediately. Fungal growths begin to decline.

I solved the problem of my own iron deficiency back in 1934 by changing my diet, and later incorporated ferrous sulphate as a blood tonic into my formula for the food supplement. It has kept me healthy all these years, and many other people as well, judging by their phone calls and letters (see *Testimonies*, Appendix A). It should be said that my treatment is a natural one which is "not financially costly" and is "not harmful", to quote two of the criteria which the Anti-Cancer Council of Victoria says it uses to recognise alternative treatments (to chemotherapy and so on).

For someone with a virulent tumor contemplating surgery and chemotherapy or suffering their aftermath, I would say do not delay getting on to a balanced diet and removing pollutants from your food and environment. That will give your body a chance against the pathogens. Taking my alkaline salts as a food supplement has the effect of neutralising acids in which these organisms flourish and supplying minerals needed for making new blood.

If you are losing the battle because organisms like Fasciolopsis and clostridium are multiplying in their millions and taking over your body, that is, you have cancer, then killing them should be your top priority. And that is where the walnuts come in. It is greatly encouraging to me to realise that the trees I planted and have nurtured for more than 60 years may be about to play a crucial role in the treatment of a disease which has stolen more years of life from our population than any other and is now the No. 1 killer of Australians.*

BLACK-WALNUT TINCTURE

TINCTURE of black-walnut hull, according to my reading, can quickly kill not just Fasciolopsis but several dozen other parasites and their stages that live in us, and in our household pets, when combined with two herbs: the leaves of the wormwood shrub and the common spice,

* "New cases of cancer are increasing in Australia at a rate of two percent each year. Our population is ageing and cancer has already overtaken heart disease as the No. 1 killer of Australians. Cancer is the major cause of premature loss of life — it has stolen more years of life from our population than any other disease." — Prof Robert Burton, Director, Anti-Cancer Council of Victoria web (Internet) site, December 1999.

cloves. That is something no tablet from the chemist can do safely and effectively. Wormwood shrub is also known as Artemisia.

Hulda Clark's pesticide recipe is reproduced in her book*. As a traditional remedy, it kills parasites without causing headaches or nausea, and without interfering with chemotherapy or other clinical treatment for cancer. As a bonus it also despatches aggressive and unwanted germs of the digestive tract such as salmonella, shigella and clostridium. The green hulls of *Juglans nigra* are available on the tree in the southern hemisphere from late December to early February.

If the herbs do their jobs, Fasciolopsis should be dead within a week. Dr Clark has other treatments to get encysted parasites and hydatid sand out of the body such as kidney and liver herbs, and you can read about those in her book.

Details of where to get the herbs are published on the Internet site www.healthastute.com.

To stay healthy, however, there is no substitute for eating fresh foods and avoiding nutritionally unbalanced foods and foods likely to be polluted. That is why I commend to everybody a supplement to the present book, a 120-page reference in full color entitled *Percy Weston's Cancer-Fighting Foods*, from Book Bin Publishing (see Appendix D).

THE FUTURE

I WAS once challenged to prove my theory that excessive phosphorus in the food chain has brought on the epidemic of cancer we have witnessed in the latter half of the 20th century, and all the other new diseases. My reply was that I merely present the evidence as best I can; it is for others to prove.

As we move into the 21st century I trust the present book will galvanise researchers into action to duplicate my experiments and verify the results so that the present dangerous farming practices change before it is too late for our children and grandchildren.

---

* The Cure for All Cancers, New Century Press, available from Book Bin

Publisher's footnote

PERCY WESTON is well-known for his public-spirited contributions to his community. All his adult life he seems to have taken a leading role in debate and discussion about the practical issues of living with nature.

With his conservation credentials he was a founding member 58 years ago of the Murray Valley League, whose efforts have led to a great many improvements in the life of the community bordering the river, and of the river itself. He was honored by the league upon his retirement in 1999. Closer to home, Mr Weston's first-hand knowledge of life in the early days of settlement keeps him in demand as a speaker at meetings of both Bright Historical Society, where he has been an active member for 25 years, and of Myrtleford Historical Society, about 20 years.

He's been an inveterate attender of public meetings about health issues, nor do professional audiences faze him. In April 1997 he flew to Darwin to attend the two-day World Cancer Congress by invitation of the organisers. His brief address presenting his proofs for the cause of cancer was well received by delegates, judging by their applause. To assist support groups he has given freely of his time in the hope of alleviating people's suffering. Lively and topical have been the articles about him or by him published in the daily *Border Mail* newspaper, and he is no stranger to the TV camera, regional and national.

In 1999, months after being interviewed by the regional news service about his views on fertiliser misuse, he took the initiative in contacting ABC-TV about his cancer treatment. The result was a segment that went to air on the national 7.30 Report. He says he regrets not being allowed to reply to the more than 100 people whose letters were forwarded by the ABC — for legal reasons associated with a desist directive he received from the Therapeutic Goods Administration after the program went to air.

His success and skill as a horticulturalist are apparent in the quality of the thousands of majestic walnut and chestnut trees he grafted on to sturdy root stock which are now thriving on his own land and at distant plantings. He has a knowledge and eloquence about horticulture that makes a lasting impression, but unfortunately, by his choice, is dealt with in this book only in passing.

We believe, with him, that his greatest legacy may be the discoveries documented in this book to an understanding of the present health malaise and the limitations of the intensive farming practices that have brought it on. He has both pointed out the problem and come up with the remedy.

You may well ask how a nonagenarian is able to remember all those dates and details. Well, as he revealed to us only recently, the author has kept a diary since 1936, and he has double-checked! In fact he has a dusty old cupboard full of diaries. Also we are fortunate that some longer sections, such as the events of the hormone disaster and the treatment of cot deaths, were written up originally for, respectively, an inquiry into herbicide use and a talk he gave to a SIDS foundation .

In a clear, steady hand he began writing the book four or five years ago and had completed most of the historical parts inside 18 months despite a busy schedule on the farm, even including, at certain times of the year, being on shotgun duty. By this we mean standing outside with firearm poised and blasting away whenever a white cloud of hungry sulphur-crested cockatoos looked like descending on the walnut trees.

Additional chapters took longer to compile as he thought to add the story of the 1922 Buffalo cattle heist and double murder and to comment on scientific developments as they unfolded daily via the pages of *The Age* or in the numerous books he has collected, such as Hulda Clark's. We helped with some of the research, such as the deaths-in-cattle and other statistics and the section on pathogens in the appendix. Some sections of the narrative, added during editing, expand on interesting incidents and details of farm life and grew out of impromptu question-and-answer sessions with the author. Such interviews were always punctuated by visitors calling in for walnuts or chestnuts or advice on health problems, or by telephone callers . . . all of whom Percy promptly attended to. Percy's visitors' book has hundreds of entries. He especially likes to keep in touch with the many people to whom he has supplied his anti-cancer powder.

By the end of 1999 the present book was ready for final editing and typesetting. On our visit to the author at Easter 2000, five months before his 97th birthday, to show him the proofs, Percy told us matter-of-factly about a "spill" he had had down at the dam while checking the water level. Padding about on bare feet, as is his wont, he had slipped on the wet grass, fallen forward and hit his forehead hard on a rock. (Again!) Stunned and bruised, he was otherwise unhurt and mentally alert, but said he now could not stop his eyes watering.

In June, after being taken to an ophthalmologist by his daughter, he was optimistic about a full recovery, but not so chipper when we next spoke a week later. He had been advised his driving licence was cancelled, spelling the loss of his much cherished independence and mobility.

He remained in his element on his well-kept farm, surrounded by the sights and sounds of nature, by his vegetable garden, green orchards, nut grove and paddocks of grazing sheep, until another fall in the spring of 2002 convinced his family he should no longer live alone. In April he moved into the comparative luxury of a retirement village on the banks of the Ovens River a few kilometres away, a friendly place where life moves at a leisurely pace, meals are served and visitors welcomed. He goes home on Sundays to oversee the farmwork.

Many who have called in at the farm, perhaps to buy nuts, have stayed for a chat with Percy about health matters. Returning home they have put his advice into action and found it works. For others, the insights Percy Weston offers in this book will undoubtedly provide much food for thought.

Appendix A

Letters to the Author

Margaret Richardson, of Highton, writes:

I was very sick. I had lost 3¹/₂ stone and looked and felt terrible. I could not eat.

I was being treated by a doctor for pneumonia and he sent me for X-rays. They showed up spots on the lung and liver, so he then sent me for a CAT scan, which showed the same results. He said I had cancer and wanted to start treatment right away.

I then heard of your powder, so we came up to see you. I felt positive after talking to you that I could be cured, so we bought some powder.

I then told my doctor I would take your powder for three months before I would have any other treatment. After two months I then got pneumonia again, so I was sent for more X-rays which showed up clear. The doctor was amazed. He asked me was I taking any other medicine than the powder? I said no. He then sent me for more CAT scans, which also showed up clear. I have got the two lots of CAT scans here for evidence.

I take your powder every morning in lemon or apple juice and have mainly stuck to your diet.

After about three weeks on your powder I started to feel better and started to eat more meals. In three months I have put back on a stone in weight and felt on top of the world.

Without Percy's powder I know in my heart I would not have seen Christmas 1998. All my friends and family can't believe how well I look.

I get cross that the medical profession have not done anything about your powder.

I remain ever grateful,

(25 September 1999)

Guy Webster, of Wodonga, writes:

My prayers are for your success. I used your powders for one month and found my health improved greatly. I stopped drinking CocaCola and consciously moved away from eating foods rich in phosphorus and to maintaining a diet free of junk food.

My wife of 20 years conceived our seventh child, a boy born without spot or blemish, who is now five months old, very healthy and growing very strong. This testimony can be verified with a photo (encl.) should to require it to update your files.

My health has enabled me to be an employee of Chapple Brothers on a casual basis because of [the] shortage of [full-time] work. My duties were carried out despite the disability of arthritis and osteoarthritis. My health is carrying without backsliding and I exercise each day and walk to maintain fitness.

Your enlightening advice has kept me in a stable condition and now blessed [us] with a son.

I recently obtained a plant water-supplement from my children and placed a small portion on some pot plants. It contained phosphorus. Two pot plants died within a few days. The third pot plant had its green, healthy leaves burnt and mutilated as cankerous sunspots appeared on them. I remembered the story of your sheep and returned to plain water to save the third pot plant.

Your theory of phosphorus is true and our own diet should be closely guarded against phosphorus. Your powders are needed by everyone to regain health and we can maintain a healthy diet by your phosphorus-reduced diet.

My declaration to you, Percy, is true and honest and my wife and I testify to this with our healthy son.

Yours sincerely,

(22 September 1999)

Bill Dean, of Werribee, writes:

In response to your letter requesting the experience I have had with your wonderful powder, may I tell you that I am delighted to share my experience with you.

I have been a massage therapist and remedial masseur for more than eight years. Prior to that I was a middle manager with Telstra. I had a cancer growth (skin cancer) on my right forearm removed by a general medical practitioner in the mid-1980s. At that time I was also suffering from gout in the joint of my right large toe. In February 1998, while attending a training course for the Neurostructional Integration Technique (NST) I met a student there who told me about Percy's powder. I decided to visit Percy and get some, which I did later in that year.

At that time I was still suffering from the gout in my right large toe joint. I also had another growth, diagnosed by a GP as skin cancer, on the medial side of the tibia of my left leg. The growth was continually enlarging. My blood pressure at that time was high (150 over 100). I was not being treated by a doctor for any specific problem at the time I was diagnosed as having the skin cancer, which I decided not to have removed. I then commenced using Percy's powder.

Although I noted the foods that carried high amounts of phosphorus, I did not pay a great deal of attention to them or did not consider altering my diet. I began taking $1/4$ teaspoon of the powder with the juice of $1/2$ a lemon (sometimes a whole lemon) every second day.

After one month I had my blood pressure taken (as I donate blood regularly) and to my surprise it was normal (130 over 84). The gout was not giving me trouble, but it was still sore to touch and there was little change in the skin cancer, although it appeared not to be increasing in size. I also felt better within myself, which I think was probably due to the lowering of my blood pressure.

After the third month my blood pressure was still about the same and the gout was less painful. I could now stand the toe being moved around more. The skin cancer had not increased any further and was showing a different look, almost like a fine scab had formed.

After the sixth month my blood pressure was still normal. I had some massage therapy done to my feet and to my surprise the mobilising of the right large toe was giving no pain. The skin cancer on the left leg had all but gone, showing only a light brown mark where it used to be.

I am now feeling better than I have ever felt for the last 10 years. I am taking the powder three times a week as a precaution to keep my health. The skin cancer mark is continually fading. I am now trying to give some attention to my diet, but the previous lack of attention could have been the reason for the slightly slower results with the skin cancer and gout. Another could be that the skin cancer and gout were at the extremities of the body. My wife is now taking the powder, also as a precautionary measure. She has been taking a $1/2$ teaspoon of powder with the juice of $1/2$ a lemon twice a week, every Monday and Friday.

Many thanks,
(22 September 1999)

John and Meta Selzer, of Ovens, write:

I am writing in response to your letter of 14th September regarding your request for information that could be of value to complete the writing of your book.

When we requested your powder it was not for a specific medical condition as such and therefore I do not have any documented evidence to present. However, we decided to go on to the powder as we had heard good reports and decided to use it as a general supplement to promote health and well-being.

After taking the powder for a few months we have noticed a definite improvement and a feeling of well-being, and therefore we intend continuing with the supplement.

We plan to order a copy of *Cancer-Fighting Foods* as well as looking forward to procuring a copy of your book, *Cancer: Cause and Cure.*

Yours faithfully,
(23 September 1999)

Nola Maher, of Beechworth, writes:

My physical condition before starting on the powder/diet: unwell. The doctor diagnosed hiatus hernia and had me on Zantac, which helped sometimes. I take ¼ teaspoon of Percy's [mineral food supplement] with lemon juice each morning. After the first month of taking the supplement I felt very well, and still am. I watch my diet, am off sugar, and get plenty of exercise and sleep.

My husband John is good and still taking the powder. Eats the same as I do.   (23 September 1999)

Bill Edney, of Bellbridge, writes:

In reply to your request regarding my cancer, you may not remember, but I came to you after I had my prostate removed. I went to you because I knew a patient in hospital who had incurable cancer, and after three or four months of taking your powder he felt on top of the world.

So, feeling completely exhausted, I tried your powder and find I am as fit now as I was years ago. As to my condition, I did experience sores in the scalp and my stools were very black, but now these have disappeared.

I deeply regret having the operation as it has left me impotent, and I believe your powder could have saved me the above embarrassment.

Wishing you all the best,   (27 September 1999)

Tracey Cardwell, of Numurkah, writes:

I am so glad you are writing to me about this book of yours. I used to be a very energetic person: in doing work and playing sport, and also excelling in school work.

I was diagnosed with cancer at Easter '98 after I suffered severe headaches, more so after playing sport. I had a CAT scan which supported this diagnosis. Immediately I was sent to Melbourne and two days later operated on. They removed a 6cm tumor. It was called a glioma glioblastoma multiforme. I then had six weeks on radiotherapy finishing in June, and then in August a course of chemotherapy once a week to December.

I started getting headaches again in January. Had another scan which showed the cancer was growing again. Operation number 2 came on 1st February. I was OK till the end of May when pressure built up again, resulting in operation No 3. Pressure again built up in mid-August (a cyst) and so operation No 4.

At the moment I'm well but my speech and talking motor skills are affected. Ever since I visited you I have taken the powder and watched my diet. I am still doing so. Whether it has helped I don't know, but I'm still alive so maybe it has.

Mum dictated this for me, as my words are very jumbled.

Yours sincerely,   (24 September 1999)

Les Taylor, 86, of Wodonga, interviewed at his home, said:

"When you find out you've got cancer it's a shock. Ten years ago I was in deep shock. The doctors told me I had prostate cancer. I knew I had trouble [because of difficulty urinating and having to get up often at night] but didn't think I was that far gone. In fact cancer had spread into the surrounding area.

"A month after the [extensive] operation I was pretty run down. I thought I was heading for the last roundup, like some of my mates who had cancer. I was seeing one of the doctors fortnightly. Then one day I had some mates around, and one fellow from Tangambalanga told me about an old bloke up Myrtleford way who had helped him a lot.

"So [former Wodonga mayor] John Macauley and I drove up to see him. Percy Weston gave us a spiel and a couple of bags of his powder. I got on to it and the next time I saw the doctor he said, 'Oh, I don't think you'll want to come and see me for a while. I'll leave it for three months.' And then he said, 'Looks as though you've gone into remission.'

"Taking the powder and restricting my diet made me feel much better. I was getting around good and proper . . . I was elected CFS fire officer for the area (Districts 24 and 26)."

Les's wife, Kathleen, who began a nursing career in 1941 at Broken Hill and worked at the urology ward of Sydney's Prince Henry's Hospital, added: "I haven't known anyone to last two years after they get secondary cancer into their bones like Les did."   (18 May 2000)

Appendix B

Detecting Pathogens

The Syncrometer™ (see Curbing Cancer Culprits, page 114) is a modified Dermatron, which is a device invented decades ago to measure body resistance (as opposed to skin resistance, which is what lie detectors measure). The idea is that you can use it to tune into the wide range of frequencies emitted by the human body — its tissues, organs and fluids — and to vibrations from microbes and substances which have entered the body.

Each Syncrometer consists of a circuit connecting a probe and handhold, loud speaker and two switched conductive test surfaces. Tests last about half a second each. On one test surface, known as the substance plate, you place the test substance. It could be something of which you have eaten or that you suspect is present in food. When the probe makes contact with the plate you hear a sound, amplified in the speaker. On the second test surface, known as the tissue plate, you place a specimen of your white blood cells and listen to the sound the probe makes. (White blood cells are easily obtained by squeezing an oil gland on your face or body and smearing a ribbon of the whitish matter on to a microscope slide or other flat surface in contact with the plate).

Identical sounds do not mean there is anything in common between the test substance and the white blood cells. Resonance does. Resonance means YES, the test is positive. Resonance in the circuit can be heard briefly as a tone quality as the sound rises quickly to a higher pitch. Resonance happens when substance and sample tissue on the test plates precisely match substance and tissue type in the body. If there is resonance between the test substance and your white blood cells, Dr Clark says it is virtually certain that the test substance is a toxin that is in your body and has shown up in your white blood cells. This is not so surprising considering it is the job of white blood cells to eliminate foreign substances from the blood by making antigens against unwanted microbes and chemicals and ingesting them.

You look for a particular parasite, solvent, elemental metal, food or product in the body by placing a known sample of it, properly labelled for identification, on the substance plate. If an agent of destruction like this is in your body in any significant quantity, chances are it will show up in your white blood cells and be heard as resonance. You can search in the body for the signatures of particular active bacteria, viruses, fungi or parasites and their products. There is no need for specimens on the substance plate to be alive, but merely present on a microscope slide or in culture sealed in a bottle or loose in a plastic bag as you probe while your other hand grips the conductive handhold.

To find out if the identified toxin or intruder has invaded a specific body organ or tissue, you place a tissue sample *corresponding* to that organ on the *tissue plate* of the Syncrometer and check for resonance. (A *corresponding* organ specimen means one such as kidney or liver or brain which can be obtained from the butcher or fishmonger to correspond with a human kidney or liver or brain and so on, since the cells of animals' organs turn out to have the same distinctive resonance as our own.) With practice, Dr Clark advises, it is possible to detect the presence of distinctive toxins and intruders in particular tissues, and her casebook is full of examples of such simple tests. She also uses the results of conventional blood tests, provided by pathology labs, as a guide to treatment.

HOW TUMORS FORM

The Syncometer detects non-food copper in all tumors, benign and malignant alike. Its build-up in the body correlates with depressed serum iron levels in patients' blood, according to blood tests. The same copper prevents iron being used by the body to make hemoglobin. Copper uses up the body's gluthione and other protein-building sulphur compounds, and causes mutations. The cancer sufferer is quite deficient in the heavy-metal detoxifier, cysteine (a precursor to gluthione).

The device also detects isopropanol in the livers of people with cancer. A liver with a reservoir of isopropanol is no longer able to trap and kill the microscopic stages of Fasciolopsis. What is the effect of these tapeworm stages slipping through? Answer: tumor formation. How? Every tumor, benign or malignant, has a tapeworm stage in the middle of it, even including warts, Dr Clark has found. Growth factors are then produced, causing the body's cells to respond by dividing into a mass of tissue, what doctors describe as a neoplasm.

She theorises that growing a tumor around a tapeworm stage may be nature's way of protecting us from it. Or, alternatively, it may be the tapeworm orchestrating growth factors for its own survival. (It makes no difference to the worm whether its host is a snail or a human being as long as it can survive and reproduce.) Certainly the human body is resilient and has ways of suppressing tumors and repairing mutations, she says. It has coped with tumorigenesis for millenia without this necessarily leading to cancer.

But something has obviously gone wrong to bring on the epidemic of tumors and cancers of the past century. Are malignant tumors something new in history, then? Is the process of tumor generation being driven by heavy-metal pollution, man-made solvents and "globetrotting" parasites? According to the combined evidence of Dr Clark's probing, all three are responsible. But what allows parasites to take hold in company with more easily identified microbes? All the accumulated evidence of Percy Weston's life on the land points to a build-up of phosphate. To use an analogy from nature, namely our polluted waterways, cancer is like an algal bloom inside the body.

And we are not finished yet. Having both aflatoxin B and isopropanol in the liver now raises the levels of human growth factor Chorionic Gonadotropin (hCG) in the liver and subsequently throughout the body, Dr Clark states. At this point the tumor in a distant organ may be benign. It may be in the cervix or prostate or lung. But if adult Fasciolopsis should be in the liver, its miracidia stage at the site of the tumor (and other stages) produce the mitotic stimulant ortho-phospho-tyrosine, and the growth becomes malignant.

What causes the initial growth of the tumor, the benign stage? Her Syncrometer has found that tapeworm stages make malonic acid, and malonic acid is known in the scientific literature[*] to cripple the body's energy-producing Krebs cycle. As well, tapeworm stages bring with them an assortment of harmful bacteria which respond to the growth

[*] The Metabolism of Tumors, Otto Warburg, translated by Frank Dickens, MA, PHD, Constable & Co Ltd, London, 1930

stimulants. They include the fungus-like Streptomyces which is present in our soils. The tricks in its repertoire include turning nitrates into nitrites, leading to nitroso compounds which can cause mutations, and suppressing the immune response of the body's T-cells.

The eggs of the common roundworm, Ascaris, come with an unwelcome set of colonists: the pathogens Rhizobium leguminosarum, Mycobacterium avium/intracellulare and Adenovirus (common cold virus). Ominously, Ascaris also neutralises the action of Vitamin C in the body.

A DANGEROUS FLUKE

Apart from its causing cancer in the presence of isopropanol, Dr Clark has other reasons for singling out Fasciolopsis. It apparently produces different diseases with other solvents. She finds it in the pancreas in the presence of methanol, causing diabetes. If the patient has absorbed benzene and the parasite is in the thymus, she can predict HIV before even checking for its marker (the presence of Protein 24 antigen) in the patient's blood test.

In Alzheimer's disease, adult Fasciolopsis is found in the brain and always in the presence of the pollutants toluene or xylene. With other solvents adults are found in the kidneys in the case of Hodgkin's disease, in the uterus in the case of endometriosis, and in the prostate in chronic prostatitis. If there are adults in your skin you could have Karposi's sarcoma, she advises.

Many other parasites add their load of new problems that the cancer sufferer can do without. Among them may be the dog hookworm *Ancylostoma caninum*, which causes fatigue, anemia and muscle ache; *Dirofilaria immitis*, also from dogs, which causes pain over the heart and irregular heartbeat; *Cryptosporidium parvum*, diarrhea; a common fluke of the pancreas from sheep and cattle, *Eurytrema pancreaticum*, diabetes; Strongyloides (filariform larva) which causes migraine headaches; the roundworm Trichiniella spiralis, from pets, which invades muscles and causes myalgia; Ascaris, from cats and dogs, which in the human lung causes asthma and, if it gets into the brain, seizures.

Appendix C
The rise of cancer in 20th-century Australia

**Deaths of persons from cancer as a proportion (%)
of estimated Australian population**

Year	Australia's Population	Cancer Deaths	Year	Australia's Population	Cancer Deaths
1891	3,177,823	1,593			
1901	3,773,801	2,401	1952	8,739,569	11,137
1904	3,984,390	2,568	1955	9,313,291	11,886
1907	4,197,037	2,940	1958	9,846,140	12,647
1910	4,425,083	3,205	1961	10,508,186	13,689
1913	4,872,059	3,603	1964	11,280,429	15,166
1916	4,875,325	3,979	1967	11,928,889	16,170
1919	5,304,422	4,421	1970	12,663,469	18,119
1922	5,633,281	5,052	1973	13,380,400	19,396
1925	5,992,084	5,477	1976	13,915,500	20,944
1928	6,336,786	6,010	1979	14,421,900	22,138
1931	6,552,606	6,589	1982	15,178,400	25,153
1934	6,705,677	7,080	1985	15,788,300	27,669
1937	6,866,590	7,691	1988	16,538,200	29,887
1940	7,032,361	8,214	1991	17,335,933	31,285
1943	7,256,765	8,870	1994	17,854,700	33,658
1946	7,500,367	9,118	1997	18,524,200	34,316
1949	8,045,570	9,930	1998	18,751,000	34,560

Source: Australian Bureau of Statistics Year Books

y-axis values: 0.30, 0.29, 0.28, 0.27, 0.26, 0.25, 0.24, 0.23, 0.22, 0.21, 0.20, 0.19, 0.18, 0.17, 0.16, 0.15, 0.14, 0.13, 0.12, 0.11, 0.10, 0.09, 0.08, 0.07, 0.06, 0.05

Adjusted for population increase, cancer is up 300% on 1901. It now affects 1 in 3 men and 1 in 4 women

x-axis: 01 04 07 10 13 16 19 22 25 28 31 34 37 40 43 46 49 52 55 58 61 64 67 70 73 76 79 82 85 88 91 94 97

Years 1901 - 1997

Country	Year	Cancers*
Australia	**1996**	**190**
Canada	1995	195
Hong Kong	1995	186
Italy	1993	205
Japan	1994	165
Netherlands	1995	214
New Zealand	1993	217
United Kingdom	1995	214
United States	1994	199
Sweden	1995	168

◀ **International comparison**

* Malignant neoplasms, standardised
rate per 100,000 population

Source: World Health Organization, 1995 and
1996 World Health Statistics Annual; ABS
Causes of Death, Australia, 1996 (3303.

Above: New Zealand had the most
deaths from cancer, Japan the least.

In the following pages we trace the rise
of cancer in animals as well as in humans
in a study based on Victoria, and draw
conclusions about a common cause. ▶

The Victorian data

Cancer in Cattle

Malignant neoplasms notified: Victoria

Year	Value
1971	3518
1972	4101
1973	4858
1974	4420
1975	6601
1976	7792
1977	8737
1978	6789
MAX	8737
MIN	3518

CANCER IN CATTLE fig.1

	1971	1972	1973	1974	1975	1976	1977	1978
9000							x	
8500								
8000						x		
7500								
7000					x			x
6500								
6000								
5500								
5000			x					
4500		x		x				
4000								
3500	x							
3000								
2500								
2000								
1500								
1000								
500								
0								

Years

Source: Department of Natural Resources & Environment, Animal Health Operations Branc

TOTAL DAIRY COWS fig.3 (a) — Victoria (Millions)

	1971	1972	1973	1974	1975	1976	1977	1978
1.280								
1.270		x	x					
1.260	x			x				
1.250								
1.240					x	x		
1.230								
1.220								
1.210								
1.200								
1.190								
1.180								
1.170						x		
1.160								
1.150								
1.140								
1.130							x	
1.120								

Years

TOTAL BEEF COWS fig.3 (b) — Victoria (Millions)

	1971	1972	1973	1974	1975	1976	1977	1978
2.110		x						
2.060			x					
2.010								
1.960								
1.910				x				
1.860								
1.810								
1.760								
1.710	x	x			x			
1.660								
1.610								
1.560								
1.510								
1.460						x		
1.410								
1.360								
1.310								x

Years

Sources: ABS, Agricultural Commodities, Australia, cat. # 71210 and 71110, Canberra; Victorian Year Book, 1972-1979.

CANCER IN CATTLE fig.2

	1979	1980	1981	1982	1983	1984	1985	1986	1987	1988	1989	1990	1991	1992	1993	1994	1995
550															x		
525														x		x	
500																	
475																	x
450																	
425																	
400												x					
375													x				
350	x																
325																	
300					x	x											
275			x	x			x	x									
250		x							x	x							
225											x						
200																	
175																	
150																	
125																	
100																	
75																	
50																	
25																	
0																	

Year	
1979	232
1980	239
1981	260
1982	272
1983	289
1984	277
1985	262
1986	255
1987	206
1988	227
1989	237
1990	383
1991	371
1992	505
1993	543
1994	514
1995	465
MAX	543
MIN	206

Years

Source: Department of Natural Resources & Environment. Animal Health Operations Branch, Bendigo.

Year	Dairy cows	Beef cows
1979	1,047,000	1,363,000
1980	1,037,000	1,394,000
1981	1,024,000	1,449,000
1982	1,024,000	1,377,000

Year	Dairy cows	Beef cows
1971	1,244,000	1,702,000
1972	1,257,000	1,730,000
1973	1,274,000	1,909,000
1974	1,244,000	2,110,000
1975	1,269,000	2,049,000
1976	1,258,000	1,715,000
1977	1,167,000	1,477,000
1978	1,125,000	1,332,000

TOTAL HERD SIZES

Year	Dairy cows	Beef cows
1983	998,000	844,000
1984	1,021,000	1,143,000
1985	1,036,000	1,111,000
1986	1,016,000	1,039,000
1987	997,000	1,078,000
1988	977,000	1,059,000
1989	990,000	1,229,000
1990	995,000	1,305,000
1991	1,000,000	1,263,000
1992	1,026,000	1,254,000
1993	1,033,000	1,237,000
1994	1,085,000	1,325,000
1995	1,113,000	1,229,000

FIGURES 1 and 2 on pages 137-138 illustrate a rising incidence of malignant tumors in cattle in Victoria. The graphs are drawn using official data gathered by the Department of Agriculture.

You can see from the graph (fig.1a) below which expresses the cancer data as a proportion of herd population, that the trend is clearly upward. This is significant because the incidence of cancer in a large sample population of cattle in the latter half of the century runs in parallel with the rise of cancer in the human population (fig. 7). It points to a common source of cancer, namely the environment and in particular the soil in which food is grown.

Cows feed on pasture top-dressed with artificial fertilisers including superphosphate. They take up an unnatural mix of elements and a minority contract malignant tumors. The mineral imbalance is passed along to humans in milk (and also via food crops grown using these methods).

It is fortunate that we have this data, which covers the years 1971 to 1995 when malignant tumors in cattle were required to be notified to the Department of Agriculture under the Stock Diseases Act 1968.

Graziers in whose animals cancer was found received compensation under the Cattle Compensation Act 1967. The compensation varied from a maximum of $120 a carcass in the early 70s and $175 by the the late 70s to a maximum of $550 by 1995s based on the market value (saleyard price) as agreed between farmer and inspector. The

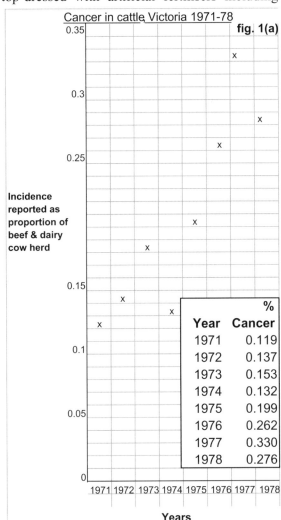

Cancer in cattle Victoria 1971-78   fig. 1(a)

Incidence reported as proportion of beef & dairy cow herd

Year	% Cancer
1971	0.119
1972	0.137
1973	0.153
1974	0.132
1975	0.199
1976	0.262
1977	0.330
1978	0.276

Years

Act was replaced in December 1995 and malignant tumor is no longer compensatible.

Figure 1 covers the years 1971-78 and figure 2 the years 1979-95, and figures 1(a) and 2(a) show the respective trends. The big drop in numbers between the graphs is due to the removal of malignant tumor of the eye, affecting mainly "pale-faced" cows, from the list of compensatible diseases from 1979. This reduced the number of notifications by about a factor of 10. It flattens the graph but does not halt the upward trend.

In interpreting the data and drawing conclusions about it, we have been careful to take into account possible distortions — factors which might have

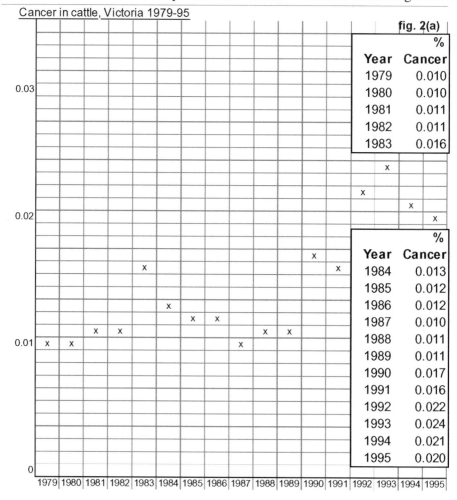

Cancer in cattle, Victoria 1979-95

fig. 2(a)

Year	% Cancer
1979	0.010
1980	0.010
1981	0.011
1982	0.011
1983	0.016

Year	% Cancer
1984	0.013
1985	0.012
1986	0.012
1987	0.010
1988	0.011
1989	0.011
1990	0.017
1991	0.016
1992	0.022
1993	0.024
1994	0.021
1995	0.020

Years

influenced farmers to notify the department that they suspected their beasts had malignant tumors.

These include: the level of compensation paid at the prevailing market prices, fluctuations in dairy and beef cattle numbers (fig.3), milk prices (fig.4), the going prices of cattle at the saleyard (fig.5), general farm costs (fig.6), and farmers' awareness of the compensation available.

DAIRY COW NUMBERS 3(c)
Victoria

Dairy Cows (millions)

Dairy Cows (millions)	1979	1980	1981	1982	1983	1984	1985	1986	1987	1988	1989	1990	1991	1992	1993	1994	1995
1.285																	
1.275																	
1.265																	
1.255																	
1.245																	
1.235																	
1.225																	
1.215																	
1.205																	
1.195																	
1.185																	
1.175																	
1.165																	
1.155																	
1.145																	
1.135																	
1.125																	
1.115																	x
1.105																	
1.095																	
1.085																x	
1.075																	
1.065																	
1.055																	
1.045	x																
1.035		x				x								x			
1.025			x	x	x								x				
1.015							x										
1.005												x					
0.995								x			x				x		
0.985										x							
0.975									x								
0.965																	
0.955																	
0.945																	
0.935																	
0.925																	
0.915																	
0.905																	
0.900																	

Years

Sources: ABS, Agricultural Commodities, Australia, cat. nos. 7121.0 and 7111.0, Canberra.   The data excludes house cows and heifers and is based on farm operations valued at $5000 or more.

FACTORS
Herd size:

During the eight years 1971-1978 (fig. 3a) Victoria's diary herd declined by 11.6 per cent. Numbers peaked at 1,274,000 in 1973, recovered from a slight dip in 1974, and fell to 1,125,000 in 1978. Notifications increased each year except in 1974 (-5%) and 1978 (-22%). For beef cows, there was a similar increase peaking at 2,110,00 in 1974 and then a steep decline to 1,332,000 by 1978, down 27.7 per cent in the period. Notifications of cancer, meanwhile, increased every year except 1974 (-9%) and 1978 (-22%).   Overall, cancer was up 132 per cent.

		ADULT FEMALE BEEF CATTLE NUMBERS fig.3 (d)																< no_of_cows >
			Victoria															
		1979	1980	1981	1982	1983	1984	1985	1986	1987	1988	1989	1990	1991	1992	1993	1994	1995
	1.445			x														
	1.435																	
	1.425																	
	1.415																	
	1.405																	
	1.395																	
	1.385																	
	1.375				x													
	1.365	x																
	1.355																	
	1.345																	
	1.335																	
	1.325																	x
	1.315																	
	1.305											x						
	1.295																	
	1.285																	
	1.275																	
	1.265														x			
	1.255															x		
	1.245																	
	1.235																x	
Beef	1.225													x				x
cows	1.215																	
(millions)	1.205																	
	1.195																	
	1.185																	
	1.175																	
	1.165																	
	1.155																	
	1.145		x				x											
	1.135																	
	1.125																	
	1.115							x										
	1.105																	
	1.095										x							
	1.085																	
	1.075									x								
	1.065																	
	1.055					x												
	1.045								x									
	1.035																	
	1.025																	

Years

Sources: A B S, Agriculture, Australia cat. no. 7113.0; A B S, Agricultural Commodities, Australia cat. Nos. 71210 and 71110, Canberra; A B A R E

In the next 16 years from 1979 to 1995 (fig. 3c) the trend to fewer dairy cows in Victoria bottomed out (1988) and the herd built up steadily to 1,113,000 in 1995, an increase of 6.3 per cent in total. However, in adult female beef cattle during 1979-1995 (fig. 3d) there was a decline of 68,000 cows (-2.8%). Notifications in these 16 years trended upward as a proportion of the herd (fig.2a). This represents a doubling in cancer and an average rate of rise in tumors of 3.1 per cent a year.

Milk prices:

Victorian milk prices were not available but, as Victoria is the nation's biggest producer, the Australian figures should provide a reliable guide. Here rising milk prices can be expected to be a disincentive for dairy farmers to report tumors in their animals (although most would not want an affected animal in the herd). The regular price increases (fig.4a) in the eight years to 1978 suggest farmers would have at least maintained their standard of living from market milk.

The upward trend continued from 1979 to 1995 (fig.4b). The notable years for price falls are 1983, 1984, 1990, 1993 and 1994. Yet there is no evidence that low milk prices in these years caused spikes in the compensation curve due to a rush of dairy farmers seeking compensation for diseased beasts (figures 2, 2a).

AUSTRALIAN MILK PRICES fig.4 (a)

Cents/litre (weighted average)

Cents/litre	1971	1972	1973	1974	1975	1976	1977	1978
11								x
10							x	
9						x		
8				x	x			
7			x					
6	x	x						

Years

Sources: ABS, *Value of Principal Agricultural Commodities Produced* , cat.No. 75010, Canberra; ABARE.

AUSTRALIAN MILK PRICES fig.4 (b)

Cents/litre (weighted average)

AUSTRALIAN MILK PRICES fig.4 (a)

Weighted average	cents/litre
1971	6.5
1972	6.7
1973	7.0
1974	8.0
1975	8.1
1976	9.2
1977	9.9
1978	11.0

fig.4 (b)

1979	12.5
1980	16.0
1981	18.6
1982	20.1
1983	19.4
1984	18.2
1985	19.6
1986	22.1
1987	23.9
1988	26.8
1989	28.6
1990	23.5
1991	24.5
1992	29.0
1993	28.2
1994	27.9
1995	31.1

1979 1980 1981 1982 1983 1984 1985 1986 1987 1988 1989 1990 1991 1992 1993 1994 1995

Years

Note: Weighted average value of manufacturing milk and market milk. From 1990 manufacturing milk price was reported net of market support. Sources: ABS, *Value of Principal Agricultural Commodities Produced*, cat. No. 7501.0, Canberra; ABARE

Saleyard prices:

Similarly, rapidly rising saleyard prices from 1975 to 1978 (fig.5a) would have been a disincentive for farmers to seek compensation. And yet the growth in compensation applications remained strong until 1978.

There was a plunge in averaged sale prices in 1981 and 1982 (fig.5b) but the compensation curve remained smooth until 1983. A smaller dip in saleyard prices in 1991 may have led to a jump in compensation claims in the following year (fig.2).

		AUSTRALIAN LIVESTOCK - SALEYARD PRICES fig.5 (a)

Cows

Cents/kg (est. dressed weight, cows 201-260 kg)

Year	cents/kg
1971	
1972	
1973	
1974	
1975	22.8
1976	32.2
1977	42.2
1978	61.2

Years

Sources: Meat and Livestock Australia Ltd, *National Livestock Report*, Sydney; ABARE.

Farm costs:

The index of total prices paid by farmers is a 45-degree line (fig.6, next page) except for a flattening out in 1989-1993. The flattening-out represents a period of reprieve from increasing farm costs. It would not of itself be a source of pressure for farmers to seek compensation for still-useful animals. It does not help to explain the steep rise of the compensation curve (fig.2) over these years.

AUSTRALIAN LIVESTOCK - SALEYARD PRICES fig.5 (b)

Cows

Cents/kg (est. dressed weight, cows 201-260 kg)

Year	cents/kg
1979	136.2
1980	131.8
1981	111.6
1982	101.2
1983	136.9
1984	149.4
1985	155.6
1986	155.2
1987	167.3
1988	179.9
1989	185.1
1990	183.3
1991	176.2
1992	174.2
1993	184.8
1994	187.0
1995	169.2

Years: 1979 1980 1981 1982 1983 1984 1985 1986 1987 1988 1989 1990 1991 1992 1993 1994 1995

Sources: Meat and Livestock Australia Ltd, *National Livestock Report*, Sydney; ABARE.

Indexes of prices paid by farmers in Australia fig.6 data

Totals

	1981	1982	1983	1984	1985	1986	1987	1988	1989	1990	1991	1992	1993	1994	1995
Materials and services	55.5	56.6	63.1	62.6	61.5	66.3	73.4	81.6	81.7	85.3	87.4	87.8	90.2	94.1	98.7
Labor	47.7	52.3	55.8	60.0	63.0	65.6	68.5	73.5	78.9	82.7	86.5	89.7	91.0	92.3	95.1
Marketing	52.2	56.5	61.7	64.5	68.4	72.6	76.5	83.8	86.4	87.4	88.7	88.7	91.0	92.9	96.2
Overheads	54.9	65.1	69.1	73.9	85.8	94.9	93.7	110.5	126.5	119.9	109.4	96.7	94.5	101.4	109.2
Capital items	41.8	46.5	50.9	54.5	60.2	67.0	72.7	76.8	80.7	83.0	84.6	88.0	91.9	94.4	97.1
Total prices paid	49.9	55.3	59.8	63.4	68.3	74.2	77.4	84.3	90.1	90.8	90.7	89.5	91.1	94.9	99.4
Excluding capital items	52.5	57.8	62.4	65.6	70.1	74.5	77.9	85.2	91.2	91.8	91.5	89.7	91.0	95.0	99.8
Excluding capital and overheads	51.1	55.4	60.2	63.0	66.1	69.6	73.7	79.0	82.9	85.1	87.4	88.2	90.4	93.6	97.7
Excluding seed, fodder and store and breeding stock	49.6	55.8	60.2	64.2	70.0	75.7	78.3	85.0	92.0	94.0	93.1	91.9	92.5	95.1	99.3

Years

Source: ABARE.

Index of prices paid by farmers in Australia fig.6

Total prices paid (Y axis: 40 to 100)

	1981	1982	1983	1984	1985	1986	1987	1988	1989	1990	1991	1992	1993	1994	1995
100															x
94														x	
92													x		
90									x	x	x	x			
84								x							
78							x								
74						x									
68					x										
64				x											
60			x												
56		x													
50	x														

Years

Source: ABARE.

Cancer in Humans
Victoria, Australia

Deaths of Victorians due principally to malignant neoplasms (cancer):

Fig.7(a) data

Year	M + F	Population	% Cancer
1971	4,858	3,601,400	0.13
1972	4,912	3,661,300	0.13
1973	5,124	3,707,700	0.14
1974	5,250	3,755,700	0.14
1975	5,278	3,787,400	0.14
1976	5,551	3,810,400	0.15
1977	5,507	3,837,000	0.14
1978	5,723	3,863,800	0.15

Sources: ABS: Causes of Deaths, 3303.0 and 3302.0, issues 1971-1978; Victorian Year Book 1972-1979.

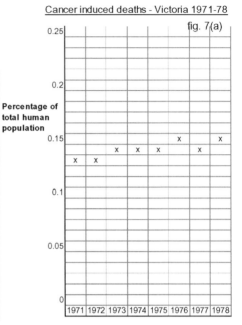

Cancer induced deaths - Victoria 1971-78   fig. 7(a)

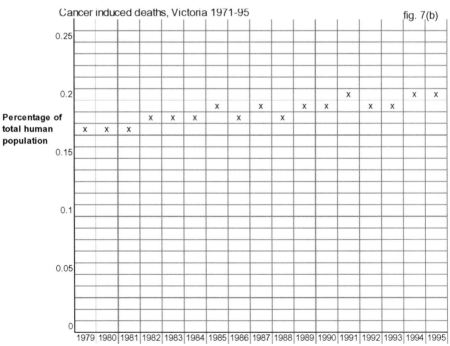

Cancer induced deaths, Victoria 1971-95   fig. 7(b)

Years

Cancer in Humans (continued from p.148)

IN TANDEM with the notification and cancer-related slaughter of 46,816 cattle in the years 1971-78, there were 42,203 registrations of Victorians certified as having died of cancer.

Notifications in the next 16 years for which figures on cattle are available began from a lower base with removal from the compensation scheme of the most common and easily treated form of cancer, lesions of the eye.

However, if the figures are regarded as at all representative of the total cattle population of the State, and evidence suggest they should be, then the inescapable conclusion is that cancer continued to increase from year to year in cattle. In fact in the 16 years to 1995, it doubled. This is the strongest of proof, if any more were needed, that Percy Weston's concerns about the excesses of commercial farming are justified.

The even more dramatic increase of cancer in the human population is borne out by Australian Bureau of Statistics figures showing cancer making up 16.6 per cent of deaths from all causes in Australia in 1971 rising to 26.9 per cent of all deaths in 1995.

In Victoria, expressed as a proportion of the population, death by cancer was 0.13 per cent in 1971 (4,858 people) and 0.20 per cent (9,166 people) in 1995. Its rate of increase was an average of 2.25 per cent a year.

This should be cause for alarm. We must move towards an ecologically sustainable form of agriculture and, on a personal level, adopt Percy's remedy to neutralise surplus phosphorus in our food.

Deaths of Victorians due principally to malignant neoplasms (cancer):

Year	M + F	Population	% Cancer
1979	6,419	3,886,400	0.17
1980	6,652	3,914,300	0.17
1981	6,765	3,946,900	0.17
1982	7,191	3,992,900	0.18
1983	7,123	4,037,600	0.18
1984	7,189	4,078,500	0.18
1985	7,723	4,120,100	0.19
1986	7,493	4,160,900	0.18
1987	7,853	4,210,000	0.19
1988	7,848	4,262,600	0.18
1989	8,185	4,320,200	0.19
1990	8,204	4,378,600	0.19
1991	8,640	4,420,400	0.20
1992	8,482	4,455,000	0.19
1993	8,649	4,472,400	0.19
1994	8,933	4,487,600	0.20
1995	9,166	4,517,400	0.20
1996	9,060	4,560,200	0.20
1997	9,043	4,605,100	0.20
1998	8,961	4,660,900	0.19

Fig.7(b) data

Sources: ABS: *Causes of Deaths*, 3303.0, 3302.0, issues 1979-1995; Victorian Year Book.

Cancer in Humans
Recent past — cancer by age group

1998

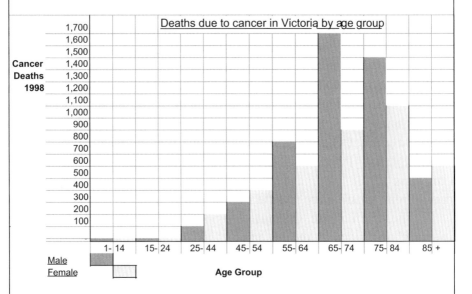

Cancer deaths as a percentage of total deaths (M/ F) due to all causes in each age group:

	1- 14	15- 24	25- 44	45- 54	55- 64	65- 74	75- 84	85 +
Male	27.5 %	4.4 %	14.9 %	34.9 %	45.9 %	41.2 %	28.7 %	18.4 %
Female	22.7 %	16.4 %	37.6 %	61.1 %	55.4 %	42.0 %	23.3 %	10.9 %

Deaths from cancer:

Age group	Male	Female
1-14	25	17
15-24	13	18
25-44	144	180
45-54	316	371
55-64	793	563
65-74	1,674	1,000
75-84	1,498	1,166
85+	549	632
All ages	5,077	4,017

Deaths from all causes:

Age group	Total M	Total F
1-14	91	75
15-24	297	110
25-44	966	479
45-54	906	607
55-64	1,727	1,017
65-74	4,062	2,383
75-84	5,214	4,996
85+	2,989	5,802
All ages	16,407	15,600

Appendix D
Cancer — then and now
Victoria, 1870

In terms of the five leading causes of death according to age group in 1870 in Victoria, cancer in males rates a mention only in the age groups 55-64 years and 65-74 years. Seven per cent and 5 per cent respectively died from it, according to records required to be kept by the colonial Government of the time. (The four more prominent causes given of male deaths in the 65-74 group are: heart disease, accident or negligence, phthisis [pulmonary tuberculosis] and apoplexy.) Although men smoked regularly, lung cancer is not referred to.

Among women, cancer is also among the top five causes of death in these age groups, but also prominent in among the 35- to 44-year-olds. Among infants, the top five killers are diarrhoea, diphtheria, teething, accident or negligence, and infantile fever.

Source: Economic and Social Commission for Asia and the Pacific, Population of Australia Vol. 1

Australia, 1920

In 1920 in Australia overall, deaths due to heart disease and senile debility outweigh deaths from cancer. "Violence" and tuberculosis are next in importance for males and tuberculosis and "congestion, haemorrhage and softening of the brain" in females. As a percentage of all deaths (32,053 male and 24,236 female) for each sex:

Age group:	35-44	45-54	55-64	65-74	75+
Cancer, men:	0.4%	1.2%	2.4%	2.0%	0.9%
Cancer, women:	0.5%	1.6%	3.2%	2.6%	1.2%

Source: ABS Official Year Book 1921

Australia, 1963

In 1963 in Australia overall, deaths due to heart disease outnumber deaths from cancer. Next in significance are vascular lesions. As a percentage of all deaths (53,212 male and 41,682 female) for each sex:

Age group:	35-44	45-54	55-64	65-74	75+
Cancer, men:	0.6%	1.7%	3.5%	4.4%	3.6%
Cancer, women:	1.1%	2.3%	3.3%	3.9%	4.4%

Lung cancer accounts for 2,121 deaths — 1,859 males, 262 females, or about 16% of total cancer deaths.   Source: ABS

Australia, 1978

In 1978 in Australia overall, deaths due to heart disease continue to out-number deaths from cancer. Next in significance is cerebrovascular disease. As a percentage of all deaths (60,281 male and 48,144 female) for each sex:

Age group:	35-44	45-54	55-64	65-74	75+
Cancer, men:	0.6%	2.1%	4.9%	6.8%	5.6%
Cancer, women:	0.4%	2.4%	4.4%	5.0%	6.3%

Tumors of the digestive system cause the most deaths (32%) from cancer, followed by lung cancer (21%, prodominantly in men) and breast cancer (8%)

Source: ABS

Australia, 1998

In 1998 in Australia overall, cancer deaths now outnumber deaths from ischaemic heart disease (but not diseases of the circulatory system). As a percentage of all deaths (67,066 male and 60,128 female) for each sex:

Age group:	25-44	45-54	55-64	65-74	75+
Cancer, men:	0.9%	2.1%	4.8%	9.6%	11.6%
Cancer, women:	1.2%	2.4%	3.7%	6.3%	11.1%

Tumors of the digestive system caused the most deaths (27%) from cancer, followed by lung cancer (18%). Source: ABS

Fertiliser use and abuse

At the turn of the century crops were manured in Victoria mostly by animal dung. Only one part in 6 or 7 parts comprised artificial fertiliser, a term that describes everything from rock phosphate from Oceania and nitrates from Chile to bonedust from colonial India. It did not take long for farmers to realise that productivity gains could be had from the new fertilisers, and with governments offering incentives, the ratio had shrunk to 1:1 by 1922. Superphosphate is made from phosphate rock by reaction with sulphuric acid, and in 1938 the value of rock phosphate imported represented 71 per cent of the total imports of fertilisers. By 1976 the production and use of animal manures in Australia was "insignificant" according to the Australian Bureau of Statistics Year Book. By then superphosphate comprised about 85 per cent of Victoria's annual usage of fertilisers. (The main other artificial fertilisers manufactured comprised urea, ammonium nitrate, calcium ammonium nitrate, urea formaldehyde and anhydrous ammonia.)

Large quantities of super are spread on cereal crops and more than half (well over 400,000 tonnes a year in Victoria) on pastures in areas of good to moderate rainfall. Apart from phosphorus, super also contains sulphur, in which most Australian soils are deficient. Potassium deficiency in Australia is confined mainly to soils in higher rainfall areas which are intensively cropped.

When applied to excess via artificial fertilisers, researchers say, the inorganic ions orthophosphate, nitrate, sulphate and potassium will accumulate in storage pools in various plant tissues (Barraclough 1993). In a Queensland study of the pasture herb Siratro in 1970, agricultural scientists White and Haydock found that critical phosphorus concentration in young runners ranged from 0.16% to 0.29%. The most important factor associated with this dramatic variation in uptake was rainfall in the 28 days before harvest. Such discoveries in the field of plant nutrition could help farmers to minimise and optimise their use of artificial fertilisers, for the health and well-being of consumers.

Cause of cattle bloat

Researchers have identified particular types of pasture and inappropriate fertiliser application as leading to bloat, which is a form of indigestion in cattle.

Gases are produced normally in the animal's rumen and reticulum by microbial action during digestion and are eliminated by eruction (belching). Bloat is the condition that occurs when the animal cannot eliminate the gases of fermentation and pressure builds up, affecting breathing and heart function. The gases not eructed may form a foam or froth in the rumen which further prevents elimination. Bloat is visible as a swelling in the left flank, between the left hip and ribs.

Pastures comprised of more than 50 per cent legumes, especially if irrigated and heavily top-dressed, are most likely to cause bloat. Some legumes, such as lucerne and subterranean clover, cause bloat problems while others, such as serradella and cowpea, apparently do not.

Why should there be this difference? Clovers, like other plants, have some 100,000 genes and some are better at taking up certain minerals than others. The legumes causing problems may be better at uptake of potassium, nitrogen, etc. Consequently, if excessive fertiliser is applied by the farmer, the plant may look lush and grow quickly but will be minerally deficient. And this can trigger reactions in the cow's stomach.

A pharmacist, L. A. Campbell, has described in a 1996 Waikato Farm Discussion Group paper how New Zealand farmers, in their quest for increased production, have applied copious amounts of potassic fertiliser to their paddocks, not realising that potassium (K) levels decrease sodium (Na) uptake in pastures. The ideal ratio for K:Na, he said, was 7:1. Yet in hundreds of analyses performed on pastures causing bloat, he had found ratios of 40:1 to 75:1 to be common. As a detergent chemist, he believed the cause of the stable, persistent foam in bloated animals to be due to an excess of potassium in combination with excess nitrogen from high-protein legumes (especially if fertilised with excessive nitrogen fertiliser such as urea, which actually inhibits normal nitrogen fixing by the plant itself). Excess nitrogen also would form ammonia in the rumen, causing added stress to the animal.

Canadian research had demonstrated that bloat-prone animals had low ruminal sodium and high potassium concentrations. Quoting researchers Malins and Grunes (1977) he said potassium, in combination with excess nitrogen, had been found to exacerbate a loss of magnesium in the animal's blood. And magnesium is one of the essential alkaline elements you need to balance phosporus (see 'The War Years' and 'Designer Cure'). Calcium uptake also was affected.

Grasses regularly found to cause bloat problems are the temperate legumes lucerne (also known as alfalfa), barrel medics, snail medics, black medic, common burr medic, woolly burr medic, cluster clover, red clover, rose clover, shaftal clover, strawberry clover, subterranean clover, and white clover.

Analysis* of a kilo of *Medicago sativa* (lucerne):

Ca	P	Mg	K	Na	N	Cl	S	Fe	Cu	Zn	Mo	B
2.0%	0.4%	0.85%	4.5%	0.6%	6.0%	1.7%	0.4%	60mg	15mg	40mg	10mg	60mg

Legumes causing low or no bloat problems are: burseem clover, serradella, woolly-pod vetch, and the tropical legumes cowpea, lablab, leucaena, desmanthus, stylos and siratro.

Analysis* of a kilo of *Lablab purpureus*:

Ca	P	Mg	K	Na	N	Cl	S	Fe	Cu	Zn	Mo	B
1.7%	0.5%	0.65%	1.8%	-	5.3%	-	0.35%	-	20mg	70mg	1.0mg	50mg

---

* From *Plant Analysis Interpretation Manual*, Reuter & Robinson, CSIRO 1997. Figures are for specimens taken at early flowering and are at the high end of the range for content of each element.

Hormonal drugs and cancer

The harmful long-term effects on women of taking the hormonal oral contraceptive Pill became clear in 1988 with the publication in Britain of a comprehensive study in *The Lancet*. The researchers, Beral and Hannaford, looked at the medical data on 47,000 women and took into account their age, social class, number of children, smoking, and many other factors. Their conclusion: women who had been taking the Pill for 10 or more years were three times more likely to develop cervical cancer than non-users.

And a Sydney-based study, by Brock and co-workers, published in 1989 in the *Medical Journal of Australia* reported a 130 per cent increased risk of cancer with use of the Pill for more than six years. It also found that promiscuity greatly increased the risk of cervical cancer, as did early age at first intercourse. However, a protective effect was found for women who practised natural family planning, which is based on observation of a woman's fertility indicators.

Short-term use of the Pill also has its problems. In 1983 Pike and Henderson reported in *The Lancet* that in women under 25 years of age, using the Pill for one to 24 months increased the risk of breast cancer by 40 per cent compared with non-users. The risk jumped to 140 per cent when used for 25-48 months and to 310 per cent for use over five years.

So much for its carcinogenic impact. Ten years earlier, a report from the Boston Collaborative Drug Surveillance Program noted that there was a 1,000 per cent increased risk of blood clots for Pill users, compared with non-users. And in 1981, Layde and Beral reported that circulatory disease had risen 320 per cent in 23,000 women who had taken the Pill during 1968-69. The more modern "micro" pills do not diminish the risk but appear to be just as dangerous as older prescriptions.

The above studies are among 278 best-practice research findings published in the world's leading medical journals between 1972 and 1996 that are summarised in *A Consumer's Guide to the Pill and Other Drugs*, by pharmacist John Wilks, published in Australia by TGB Books. After reviewing this mass of evidence against the Pill, Mr Wilks laments the "drug-induced vandalism of the female physiology" by its promoters. The weight of research clearly indicates that the Pill at an early age is particularly dangerous, with nearly five times the risk of breast cancer reported for teenagers taking the Pill than non-users.

For the Pill produces its carcinogenic effects whether or not a woman has a genetic predisposition to a particular disease. The reason may well be nutrition. As pointed out in the book, *Percy Weston's Cancer-Fighting Foods*, the Pill disrupts the functions of some essential vitamins. It blocks the action of pyroxidine, needed for a healthy central nervous system and for protein building, and the action of the antioxidant vitamin tocopherols, and it retards the action of riboflavin, the vitamin needed for synthesis of amino acids and fatty acids.

The argument against the Pill also applies to hormone replacement therapy. Whatever benefit these artificially derived hormones offer a woman after menopause in terms of protection against heart disease and osteoporosis is lost withing seven years of ceasing therapy, according to Colditz (J. Soc. Gynaecol. Invest. 1996), quoted by Mr Wilks. Long-term, hormone replacement therapy increases cancer risks. Such that Dr Colditz asks, "Should breast cancer be the price we pay for reduced risk of heart disease and fracture?" Answer: Not while we can use diet and excercise.

New book from Book Bin Publishing rates our foods

THE diagnosis is cancer. What is the first thing the doctor will recommend? "I want you to change your diet."

Percy Weston's
Cancer-Fighting Foods
Your guide to complete nutrition

Unfortunately, research into the cause of cancer and arthritis has been painfully slow. Nevertheless, all the big surveys of human populations in recent times have found a strong link between cancer and diet. As a result, most nutritionists now advocate that we eat fresh fruit and vegetables every day. But is this the full story?

Many of the foods we eat nowadays come off the farm loaded with phosphorus or lacking in alkali minerals, or both. In other words, you can't rely on them. Modern foods, and especially processed foods, are nutritionally unbalanced. They make you sick. They can lead to nutritional deficiency diseases, and at the same time faulty immune systems.

What can you do? Well for many years Percy Weston has used a chart which gives the phosphorus content of common foods in millegrams per 100 grams. Following it has saved his life several times. It showed him how to switch from foods that were making him anaemic to foods with better mineral values. He has gone on to supplement with 1/3 teaspoon every couple of days of a powder he makes up from mineral salts and takes in lemon juice.

The powder is claimed in his Australian Patent No. 518,393 to prevent and/or cure cancer when taken in association with a diet containing foods having a relatively high calcium to phosphorus ratio, and

significant sodium, magnesium and potassium. The mixture contains alkali minerals and is designed to neutralise surplus phosphorus in the body — the cause of the trouble.

Following the diet, that is, choosing foods with good natural mineral balance and judiciously combining foods to make up for deficiencies, is the rest of Percy's recipe for good health. And it's no surprise that fruit and vegetables (although not all of them) give the safest analyses.

It's all very well for a chemistry-loving farmer to plan meals by numbers, but what about the rest of us? For the rest of us, Health Research Pty Ltd, in association with Book Bin Publishing, has produced a 120-page book that makes all this easy to understand. It rates and ranks hundreds of foods according their mineral balance by number (Percy's Rating) but also by using a simple color code for telling at a glance whether they are harmful or helpful. Each food included has been analysed by chemists at the world's leading testing laboratories in England, Australia and the US, and the list is as comprehensive — and relevant — as those resources allow. There are five main charts:

At A Glance ranges across the common food groups such as cereals, meats, fish, nuts, vegetables, eggs, milk

and fruit, beverages, milk, fats & oils, additives, herbs and spreads.

Raw Foods (Minerals) is alphabetical and shows by means of stars just how naturally rich or poor each food is in essential minerals, and also rates it for percentage content of essential fatty acids per 100 grams.

Health Research Pty Ltd

Clarification: Health Research Pty Ltd has a product named *rhomanga*™ (see note on page 43) in tablet form. On advice from Percy Weston and a leading chemist, *rhomanga*™ is formulated to be similar to Percy's powder – in terms of its mineral content and in the critical ratios of those minerals – within the limits and constraints of the Therapeutic Goods Regulations. Also *rhomanga*™ contains added essential vitamins and is manufactured and listed for sale under the strict conditions of a pharmaceutical.

Health Research neither claims nor infers for *rhomanga*™ any of the therapeutic benefits reported for Percy Weston's powder in this book.

Health Research takes an holistic approach to well-being. Dietary supplements are only necessary to correct imbalance in the modern diet. And so the company takes an active role, especially via the printed word, in promoting public awareness of the benefits of a minerally balanced diet containing adequate fresh fruit and vegetables, as championed by Percy Weston and latterly as recommended by health authorities after the recent overwhelming epidemiological evidence linking cancer and diet.

The company is proud to lend its support to publication of the fruits of Percy Weston's life's labors — this magnificent restrospective on cancer over the past century that sheds so much light on its cause and prevention.

For details of Health Research products and services, please
telephone (61) 08 8410 1765, fax 08 8212 1747
write c/- Post Office Box 6241 Halifax Street, South Australia 5000,
or *find us* on the Internet @ www.healthastute.com
email: sales@healthastute.com

Raw Foods (Vitamins)

indicates which essential vitamins would normally be present in the same given quantity of the food.

Processed Foods applies Percy's

Rating to Australian and British commercially produced foods, where chemical analyses were available.

Ethnic Foods applies Percy's Rating

to Asian and international cooking, and to Chinese, Greek, Italian, Lebanese, Thai and Vietnamese meals, complete with description of ingredients.

Percy Weston's *Cancer-Fighting Foods* is believed to be the first book to tackle the mineral content of foods in this unique way on such an ambitious scale — in the certain knowledge that health and well-being depend on balanced mineral nutrition. To make the point, the book also draws on recent scientific literature to discuss the roles of all the essential minerals and vitamins in keeping you healthy and what happens to the body when they are missing in food. How much of each mineral and vitamin do you need? It's set out in the full table of Recommended Daily Intake by age group as set by Australian medical authorities. Trace minerals and essential carbohydrates are also covered.

The book explains the difference between saturated fats and unsaturated fats (both mono- and poly-unsaturated) and reveals which cooking oils are most helpful to the body and which block the liver, the body's detoxifier. Another useful reference for the cook or busy housewife is a full listing of food additives approved for use in processed foods by the Australian and New Zealand Food Authority according to function. The ones to avoid are color-coded in red.

A chapter on how to choose a balanced meal deals specifically with protein-building and demonstrates how to get your essential amino acids across a wider range of foods. There's even a rating for the complementary herbs you might use in culinary experiments with safer foods.

Cancer-Fighting Foods has a couple of pages about chemicals and unnatural substances present only in trace amounts in processed food and in the environment but which can have an influence out of all proportion when they get into the bodies of sick people. They typically cause unusual symptoms and prevent cancer sufferers improving, even on the best of diets. The book tells you how to avoid toxic stuff. It does not specifically question the meat-and-two-veg. approach to the main meal of the day, but leaves it up to the reader. The question to ask is: Is a particular food holding back the body's ability to cure itself? A glance at the accompanying red, yellow or green code should answer that.

There is an extensive fully-illustrated guide to much of the fresh produce available from vegetable and fruit markets that ought to be high on the shopping list of the health-conscious. The emphasis is very much on "living" food in all its magnificent variety, color and character, with tips on preparation.

So there it is. Easy to read. Hundreds of foods covered, even branded ones. Color codes to give instant warning of any danger. An invaluable reference in a convenient format for the kitchen.

As a service to readers, the following titles discussed in these pages may be ordered direct from Bookbin:

☐ **Cancer-Fighting Foods** by Health Research, 46pp color A4 @ $29.95*

☐ **The Cure for All Cancers** by Hulda Regehr Clarke, 624pp @ $49.00*

☐ **A Consumer's Guide to the Pill & other Drugs**, 2nd Edition, 280pp, by John Wilks @ $26.95*

☐ and further copies of **Cancer: Cause & Cure**, by Percy Weston @ $24.95*

* Recommended prices in Australian dollars at December 2003.

Postage: within Australia is free. To elsewhere, add $15 a book. Or order via a distributor — see Bookbin web site.

How to order:

(1) Phone freecall 1800 657 744 or (61 8) 8410 5888
(Have your credit card handy)

OR

(2) If the book is in stock, send a cheque or money order with this page to:
Bookbin Publishing, 165 Franklin Street, Adelaide South Australia 5000, enclosing your details at right

OR

(3) Order over the Internet from Bookbin's secure site:
www.bookbin.com.au   email: sales@bookbin.com.au

Name: ....   Phone: ....

Address: ....

....   Dated: ....

Indicate the book(s) and number of copies of each you wish to order by writing a number in the box beside its title, above. Allow 10 days for delivery.

I enclose (total incl.post) $ _____   Signed: _____

Free **food chart** A color-coded food chart approved by Percy Weston together with other product information will be sent free to any reader requesting it who shows proof of purchase of this book by sending this page (or photocopy thereof) to Health Research, PO Box 6241 Halifax Street, South Australia 5000. Just tick the box at right. Please include full name and address. ☐

INDEX

2,4D and 2,4,5T, page 67
Aflatoxins, 120
Aldrin, 44-45
Alzheimer's disease, 107
Anaemia, 24, 31
Aneurisms, 107
Antioxidants, 109-111
Arthritis
    in sheep, 30
    in humans 35, 37, 107
ATP and ADP, 99
Bandicoot, long-nosed, 92
Baron von Mueller, 47
Bat, Large Forest, 95
Bloat in cattle, 81, Appendix D
BCG vaccine, 98
Bogong High Plains, 18, 35
Bradley, Bonnie, 47-52, 57-
58,   89
Brandt, Johanna, 102
Broughton, Dr Peter, 68
Brady's Confidence Dredge, 6
Brych, Dr Milan, 98
Buckland
    gold diggings, 4
    cemetery, 5
Bush rat, 96
Cadmium, 116
Cancer
    definition, v, sarcoma, 43
    in sheep, 30
    in cattle, 105, Appendix C
    in humans, Appendix C, D
Cardiomyopathy, 107
Chlorine, 46
Cigarettes
    Milo, 6, 18
    Virginia leaf, 19
    chemical hazards, 112-114
Cilento, Dr Ruth, 102
Clark, Dr Hulda Regehr, 115
Codling moth trap, 112
Codliver oil, 41
Columbus, Christopher, 19
Clostridium, 63, 120
DDT, 44-46
Diabetes, 107
Dieldrin, 44-45, 105
Dingo, 34-35, 96
DuPain, 25, 37
Eccles, Prof Ron, 101

Echidna, 92
Epsom salts, 41, 116
Eurobin State School, 8
Fertiliser, guano, 20
Fitzgerald
    Catherine, 4
    Jim and Percy, 6
Fleming, Ray, 35
Forbes, Dr Alex, 101
Fox, 96
Finkel, Dr Maurice, 88
Free radicals, 110
Gawler, Dr Ian, 96
Gerson, Dr Max, 102
Gusathion, 44, 46
Gliders, marsupial, 95
Health Research, 43,158, 160
Heliothis grub, 23, 44
Hormones, artificial, 65-71,
    & cancer, Appendix D
Human genetic potential, 109
Irritable bowel syndrome, 118
Insects, sucking, 23
    thrip, aphid, jacid, 46
Issells, Dr Josef, 98
Juglans nigra (walnut) 114-116
Kangaroo, Eastern grey, 95
Kelly, Dr J.J., 24, 43
King, F.H., 103
Laetrile, 102
Lindane, 44-45
Looper moth, 44
Maguire, Dr Leo, 87
Malathion, 44, 46
Matches, wax, 2
Meares, Dr Ainslie, 101
Mice, 21-22
Milk, cows, pasteurised, 77-81
Mineral supplements, 107-108
Mopoke, 95
Mulholland, James, Len,
    Reg, 29
Mumps, 14
Mutations, 110
Mt Buffalo, 34
Mt Howett station, 12, 16
Myxomatosis, 95
Nelson Creek, 15
Nicotine, 45
Noxious weeds, 65
Osteoporosis, 107
O'Sullivan, Dr Dick, 49, 53-55
Parathion, 44, 46
Parasites, 118-122

Pasture, natural, 77
Pesticides, 45
Peter MacCallum Clinic, 57
Phillips, Dr Frederick, 51
Platypus, 92
Phascogale, Brush-tailed, 92
Phosphorus pentoxide, 13
Phossey jaw, 13
Polio, 29
Porepunkah Gully, 2, 6, 8
Possum, Mountain Pygmy, 96
Price, Jack, 69
Proanthocyanidins, 111
Quoll, Spotted-tailed, 92
Rabbits, 3
Raleigh, Sir Walter, 19
Raymont, Dr Warwick, 45
Rats, 22-23
Rutherglen Research Farm, 69
Seventh Day Adventist, 25
Sheep, Corriedale, 30, 69
    licks, 62-63, 76-78, 106
Shroud of Turin, 85
SIDS (cot death) 76-82
Spanish flu epidemic, 11
Sulphates, 42, 65
Superphosphate, 7, 21, 23, 47
    paralysis from, 33
    top-dressing, 26
    vegetable plot, 29
    triple, 105
Tobacco, 17, 19-21
    diseases, 18, 24
    organic sprays, 44
Ulcers, 107
Viral diseases, 104
Wallach, Dr Joel, 106-109
Weston
    Albert, 5
    George, 5, 8, 96
    Bill, 6
    Eric, Mervyn, 6, 25, 58
    Eric and Adrian, 29
    Verna, 2, 26
    Ernie and Charlie, 12, 14
    Michael and Helen, 52, 56
    Brendan and Adrian, 58
Weeds, 24
Wombat, common, 95
Wodonga High School, 13
World Cancer Congress, 123
Wye, Billy, 15, 95
Xavier College, 11, 18
Yellow dwarf, 18, 23-24